Target Practice

Challenging Mental Computation
Grades 1–5

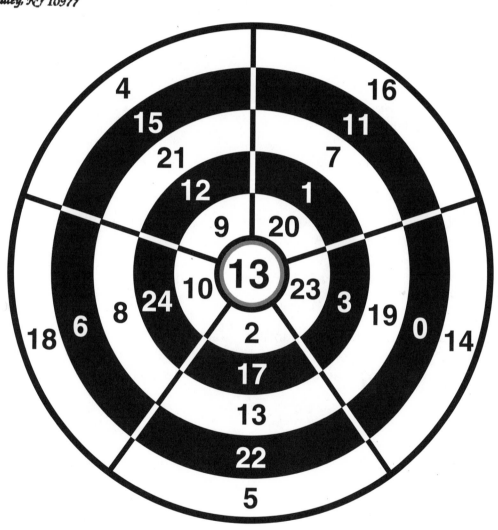

Dale Seymour • Margo Seymour

Dale Seymour Publications

Managing Editor: Michael Kane
Project Editor: Katarina Stenstedt
Production Manager: Janet Yearian
Production Coordinator: Claire Flaherty
Cover design/page design: David Woods
Text illustrations: Merle Silverman and Dale Seymour

This book is published by Dale Seymour Publications, an imprint of the Alternative
Publishing Group of Addison-Wesley.

Order number DS21226
ISBN 0-86651-735-9

2 3 4 5 6 7 8 9 10-ML-97 96 95 94 93

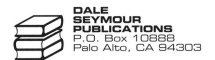

DALE
SEYMOUR
PUBLICATIONS
P.O. Box 10888
Palo Alto, CA 94303

Made from
Recycled Paper

CONTENTS

Preface .... *iv*

How to Use This Book 1

Addition and Subtraction 3

Multiplication and Division 33

Parentheses and Strategies 59

Order of Operations and Use of Parentheses 85

Target Practice™ Formats and Random Digits 93

Puzzle Solutions 119

Preface

To be sharp at mental arithmetic, one must practice it, like any other skill. Current reliance on hand-held calculators diminishes our use of mental arithmetic. Drill by itself is boring, but *Target Practice*™ puzzles are fun and challenging.

Both of us have used these types of puzzle formats in our classrooms over the past thirty years. We have found them to be most effective and motivating. *Target Practice*™ provides a challenge that catches on. We enjoy solving these puzzles and we hope you do too.

Dale and Margo Seymour
September 1992

Target Practice™ is designed to be used as a recreational diversion by one person or by a teacher in the classroom. The book can be used as a workbook or as a set of blackline masters to be photocopied to produce student worksheets. It is not intended to be used sequentially, page by page. Rather, it is a "pick and choose" book where students can choose problems at their own ability levels.

The master pages can be made into overhead transparencies and presented as a class lesson, explanation, or contest. Younger students may need help interpreting the directions. Be sure to explain terms like *horizontal* and *vertical*. The transparency master on page 61 can be used to teach the meaning of parentheses. The puzzles on pages 62 to 64 and 69 to 84 reinforce this new concept. Learning in depth about the order of operations and use of parentheses is probably not appropriate for most students using this book, but an explanation of each is presented on pages 87 and 88 for more advanced students. It is a good idea to discuss these puzzles when first introducing them to the class. Students will get the idea of the puzzles as they observe their peers coming up with solutions. Writing down solutions can come later.

Target Practice™ activities are well suited to solution by small groups. Pooling their knowledge, students teach each other informally. Sometimes they discover several right answers. They help each other record solutions correctly (and catch computation errors before writing them down).

Several formats are offered. Most progress in difficulty, sequentially. Blank format pages are offered so teachers can design their own problems. Also, students may enjoy creating their own problems as a separate challenge. Be sure to make a copy of the blank format before writing on it so you can use it as often as you like. Creative teachers can invent ways to present these puzzle ideas as class and oral activities. Contests can also be motivating if they are not given too much importance.

Transparency masters on pages 65 and 66 can be used to teach the "user-friendliness" of the numbers 1 and 0 in multiplication and addition: any number times 1 equals the original number, and any number plus 0 equals the original number. The puzzles on pages 67 and 68 illustrate this special property of the identity elements, 1 and 0.

Random Digit pages (pages 113–118) are provided as a resource. Directions can be given to provide practice at any level, for example:

"In the first four rows, find all products of 24 using two touching numbers."

"Find ten 2 x 2 squares whose digits can be used in an equation equaling 10."

"Find the largest 3-digit number on the page. Find the smallest."

"Draw a ring around a 5 x 5 square. Use this as your BINGO board."

An advanced version of *Target Practice*™, for grades 5 through 12, is also available from Dale Seymour Publications.

Addition
and
Subtraction

ADDITION AND SUBTRACTION

Circle two numbers in touching squares that add to 5. Find all you can. The numbers can be horizontal or vertical.

8		2		7		4
4	9	0	3	6	1	4	9

1
3 4
0

(5)

3
8 2
1
4

3 2 6

5   1 4 2 3

2 7 8   0   8

5 2 9 3

ADDITION AND SUBTRACTION

Circle two numbers in touching squares that add to 6. Find all you can. The numbers can be horizontal or vertical.

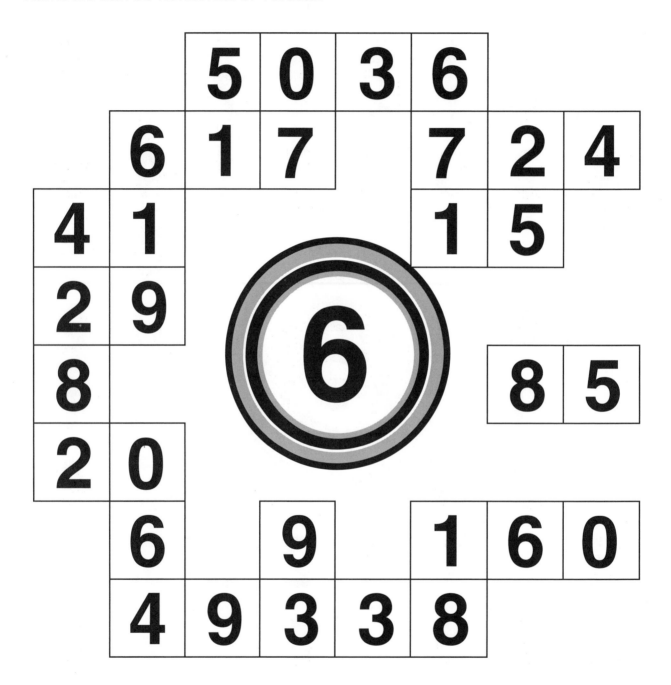

ADDITION AND SUBTRACTION

Circle two numbers in touching squares that add to 7. Find all you can. The numbers can be horizontal or vertical.

8	3	4		8	6	1	9
9		6	9	0	7		
6	1					4	3
	2		**7**		3		
3	5			1	5	3	
6	0			7		2	
0		5	2	6	1	8	6
7	2	4	7		5		

ADDITION AND SUBTRACTION

Circle two numbers in touching squares that add to 8. Find all you can. The numbers can be horizontal or vertical.

5	1	7	8	1
2 0	4	6	0	3 5
7	2			4
3	6			4
	3	8		7 1
4 4	4		1	2 9
5	8	0	4 7	4 5
6	1	2	6	3

ADDITION AND SUBTRACTION

Circle two numbers in touching squares that differ by 3. Find all you can. The numbers can be horizontal or vertical.

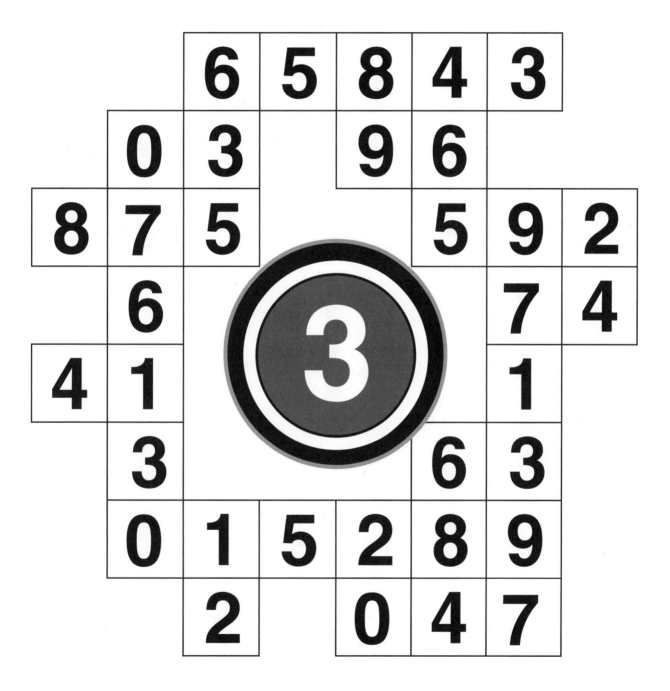

ADDITION AND SUBTRACTION

Circle two numbers in touching squares that differ by 4. Find all you can. The numbers can be horizontal or vertical.

7	3		2	9	3	9	4
	5	7	4	5	1	2	8
4		9			6	2	7
8	0		**(4)**			1	4
8	2						7
	6	6				0	
5	0	1	5	9	1	4	3
6		0	8		3	6	

ADDITION AND SUBTRACTION

Circle two numbers in touching squares that differ by 5. Find all you can. The numbers can be horizontal or vertical.

	4		2	7			3
4	9	2	6	1	5	7	8
1						4	
3	4					0	
	2		**5**			5	
3	7	6			2	6	7
5		1		1	6		
8	3	2	4	9	5	0	

ADDITION AND SUBTRACTION

Circle two numbers in touching squares that differ by 2. Find all you can. The numbers can be horizontal or vertical.

```
3 0 1     8 3
4 7 9 3 7 1 0 2
  2       4 2 6
3 5       5
  9       4 7
5 7     6 6 0
8 1 6 1 2 4   1
  2 8 0 9 5 2 4
```

(2)

ADDITION AND SUBTRACTION

Circle three numbers in a line of touching squares that add to 13. Find all you can. The numbers can be horizontal or vertical.

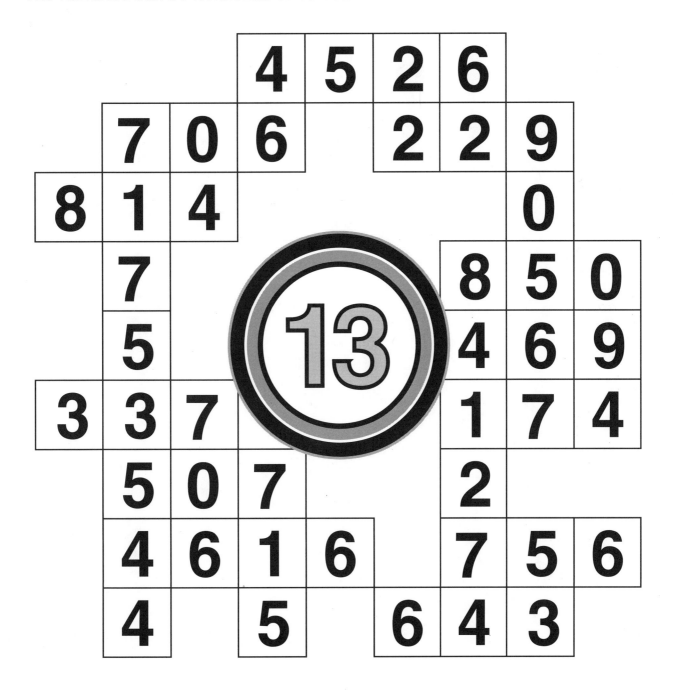

ADDITION AND SUBTRACTION

Circle three numbers in a line of touching squares that add to 14. Find all you can. The numbers can be horizontal or vertical.

9	4	4	6	5	1		8	3
3		1		4	3	9	0	5
6	0	9		5	3	4	6	6
3	4						2	1
	5		**14**				6	7
2	3	9					4	
1	9		8	3	3	1	5	8
7	0	7	2	5			3	3
6	8	2	4			7	3	4

ADDITION AND SUBTRACTION

Circle three numbers in touching squares that add to 13. Find all you can.

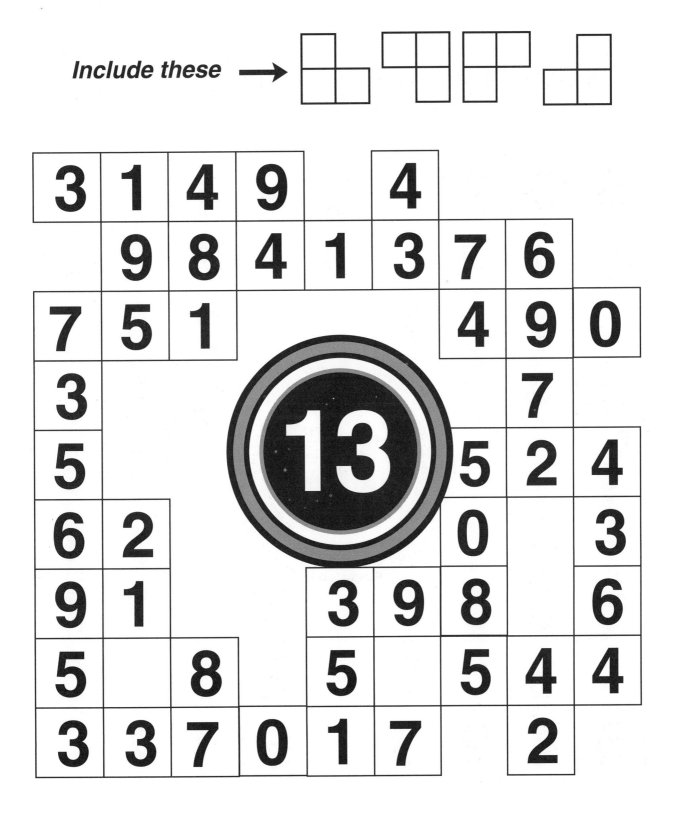

ADDITION AND SUBTRACTION

Circle three numbers in touching squares that add to 14. Find all you can.

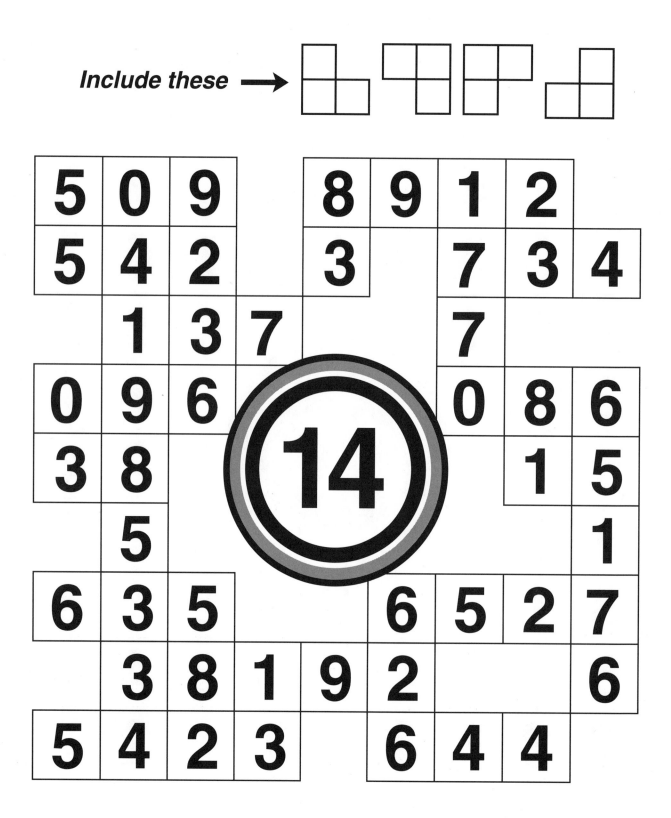

Include these ➡

ADDITION AND SUBTRACTION

Place the three numbers in the blanks, in any order, to equal the target number.

1.

___ + ___ − ___ = ___

2.

___ + ___ − ___ = ___

3.

___ + ___ − ___ = ___

4.

___ + ___ − ___ = ___

5.
___ + ___ − ___ = ___

6.

___ + ___ − ___ = ___

7.
___ + ___ − ___ = ___

8.

___ + ___ − ___ = ___

ADDITION AND SUBTRACTION

Place the three numbers in the blanks, in any order, to equal the target number.

1.
7 4 1 → **10**

___ + ___ − ___ = ___

2.
2 5 3 → **0**

___ + ___ − ___ = ___

3.
9 4 3 → **8**

___ + ___ − ___ = ___

4.
5 4 8 → **9**

___ + ___ − ___ = ___

5.
7 4 1 → **4**

___ + ___ − ___ = ___

6.
2 5 3 → **4**

___ + ___ − ___ = ___

7.
9 4 3 → **10**

___ + ___ − ___ = ___

8.
5 4 8 → **7**

___ + ___ − ___ = ___

ADDITION AND SUBTRACTION

Place the three numbers in the blanks, in any order, to equal the target number.

1.

___ + ___ − ___ = ___

2.

___ − ___ + ___ = ___

3.

___ + ___ − ___ = ___

4.

___ − ___ + ___ = ___

5.

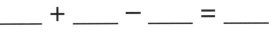

___ + ___ − ___ = ___

6.

___ + ___ − ___ = ___

7.

___ − ___ + ___ = ___

8.
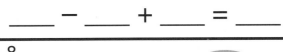
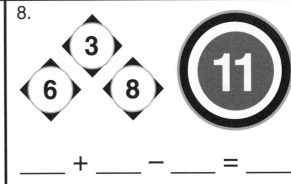

___ + ___ − ___ = ___

ADDITION AND SUBTRACTION

Place the three numbers in the blanks, in any order, to equal the target number.

1.

___ − ___ + ___ = ___

2.

___ + ___ − ___ = ___

3.

___ − ___ + ___ = ___

4.

___ + ___ − ___ = ___

5.

___ + ___ − ___ = ___

6.

___ − ___ + ___ = ___

7.

___ + ___ − ___ = ___

8.

___ − ___ + ___ = ___

ADDITION AND SUBTRACTION

Place three of the four numbers in the blanks, in any order, to equal the target number.

1.
9 7
2 6   **13**

___ + ___ − ___ = ___

2.
9 7
2 6   **11**

___ + ___ − ___ = ___

3.
9 7
2 6   **10**

___ + ___ − ___ = ___

4.
9 7
2 6   **4**

___ + ___ − ___ = ___

5.
9 7
2 6   **5**

___ + ___ − ___ = ___

6.
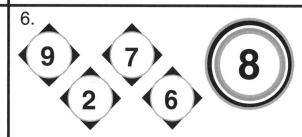

___ + ___ − ___ = ___

7.

___ + ___ − ___ = ___

8.

___ + ___ − ___ = ___

ADDITION AND SUBTRACTION

Place three of the four numbers in the blanks, in any order, to equal the target number.

1.

___ + ___ − ___ = ___

2.
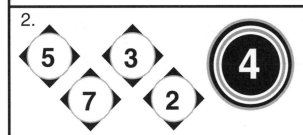

___ + ___ − ___ = ___

3.

___ + ___ − ___ = ___

4.

___ + ___ − ___ = ___

5.

___ + ___ − ___ = ___

6.

___ + ___ − ___ = ___

7.

___ + ___ − ___ = ___

8.

___ + ___ − ___ = ___

ADDITION AND SUBTRACTION

Place three of the four numbers in the blanks, in any order, to equal the target number.

1.

4　9　7　3　　**8**

____ − ____ + ____ = ____

5.

4　9　7　3　　**13**

____ + ____ − ____ = ____

2.

4　9　7　3　　**10**

____ + ____ − ____ = ____

6.

4　9　7　3　　**5**

____ − ____ + ____ = ____

3.

4　9　7　3　　**2**

____ + ____ − ____ = ____

7.

4　9　7　3　　**0**

____ − ____ − ____ = ____

4.

4　9　7　3　　**12**

____ + ____ − ____ = ____

8.

4　9　7　3　　**2**

____ − ____ − ____ = ____

ADDITION AND SUBTRACTION

Place three of the four numbers in the blanks, in any order, to equal the target number.

1.
8 7 5 3 **4**

___ − ___ + ___ = ___

5.
8 7 5 3 **10**

___ + ___ − ___ = ___

2.
8 7 5 3 **5**

___ − ___ + ___ = ___

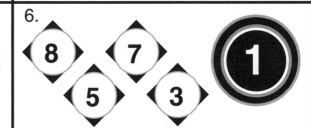

6.
8 7 5 3 **1**

___ + ___ − ___ = ___

3.
8 7 5 3 **6**

___ + ___ − ___ = ___

7.
8 7 5 3 **0**

___ − ___ − ___ = ___

4.
8 7 5 3 **12**

___ + ___ − ___ = ___

8.
8 7 5 3 **9**

___ + ___ − ___ = ___

Circle four numbers in a line of touching squares that add to 20. Find all you can. The four numbers can be horizontal or vertical.

```
0  5  9  3  9  3  4  4  1  4  1  1
1  8  4  4  4  7  2  4  8  5  6
2  6              4        5  2
0  6  6  7  1        8  8  1  3
1  0  5              5        1  5
1     2            6           8  8
4     7      (20)   0           8  8
8                   9  9  4  0  7
6  1  7  6        1           0  6
6     4     8  2  4  3        0  0
3     4        9        7     4  2  0
5  7  5  3  3  4  8  6  2  1  2
```

ADDITION AND SUBTRACTION

Circle four numbers in a line of touching squares that add to 20. Find all you can. The four numbers can be horizontal or vertical.

ADDITION AND SUBTRACTION

Circle four numbers in a line of touching squares that add to 21. Find all you can. The four numbers can be horizontal or vertical.

8	8	1	4	4	1	7	4	2		
	0	6	4		7	1	5	8	5	7
3	7	1	4		2		5	8	6	8
8	6	4	9		1		8	6	8	6
7	3						7	2	3	9
5	8			**21**					3	1
5	0	8					3	7	7	
4		8				5	6	5	5	
	0	2		8		2	6	5	2	
4	9	8	3	8	3	9	4	6	2	3
6	3	5	7	9	9		4	6	4	
8	8	7	7	6	1		7	3	2	0

ADDITION AND SUBTRACTION

Circle four numbers in a line of touching squares that add to 21. Find all you can. The four numbers can be horizontal or vertical.

0	3	4	0	3	4	2	2	6	7	6
1	5	4	1	4	5	0	9	6	3	3
4	4	8	0	1	3	1	2	1	8	2
7	9	0	5	2	3	3	7	1	3	6
0	8	9				7	9	7	5	
4	0						6	8	5	
3	3			21			5	3	5	
6	8						3	9	1	
2	1	7	6	9	8	3	8	2	1	9
5	3	1	4	4	1	6	4	5	3	0
6	5	6	7	8	9	9	4	2	5	9
1	4	1	4	9	5	3	8	5	5	1

ADDITION AND SUBTRACTION

Look at the blank squares below. Then look at the block of numbers. Find three numbers in the same position that fit into the blanks in the number sentence to equal the target number.

6	9	6	7	0	7	8	3	6	9	1
8	3	1	5	9	8	4	7	8	5	8
6	5	9	4	1	4	3	2	6	3	4
2	7	5	1	7	7	6	4	9	0	6
5	3	6	3	4	4	9	7	6	1	5

(8)

8 4
4   1.   2.

1. $\underline{8} + \underline{4} - \underline{4} = \underline{8}$

2. $\underline{} - \underline{} + \underline{} = \underline{8}$

(9)

3.   4.

3. $\underline{} + \underline{} - \underline{} = \underline{9}$

4. $\underline{} - \underline{} + \underline{} = \underline{9}$

(10)

5.   6.

5. $\underline{} + \underline{} - \underline{} = \underline{10}$

6. $\underline{} + \underline{} - \underline{} = \underline{10}$

(11)

7.   8.

7. $\underline{} + \underline{} - \underline{} = \underline{11}$

8. $\underline{} - \underline{} + \underline{} = \underline{11}$

ADDITION AND SUBTRACTION

Look at the blank squares below. Then look at the block of numbers. Find three numbers in the same position that fit into the blanks in the number sentence to equal the target number.

3	7	2	3	7	8	0	7	5	0	9
0	8	2	6	1	9	7	0	4	8	9
6	0	4	3	8	7	5	0	5	3	4
0	3	9	3	9	3	4	4	1	4	6
1	6	6	8	5	2	2	1	5	3	0

(7)

1. 2.

1. ___ + ___ − ___ = 7

2. ___ − ___ + ___ = 7

(8)

3. 4.

3. ___ + ___ − ___ = 8

4. ___ − ___ + ___ = 8

(9)

6. 5.

5. ___ + ___ − ___ = 9

6. ___ + ___ − ___ = 9

(10)

7. 8.

7. ___ + ___ − ___ = 10

8. ___ − ___ + ___ = 10

ADDITION AND SUBTRACTION

Look at the blank squares below. Then look at the block of numbers. Find three numbers in the same position that fit into the blanks in the number sentence to equal the target number.

4	8	7	4	5	4	7	6	2	6	3
2	8	8	5	6	2	8	3	8	2	2
6	0	6	3	9	5	2	3	7	0	5
7	5	0	9	0	5	8	2	6	1	1
7	0	1	3	5	8	8	1	5	9	9

8

1.

2.

1. ___ + ___ − ___ = 8

2. ___ − ___ + ___ = 8

9

3.

4.

3. ___ + ___ − ___ = 9

4. ___ − ___ + ___ = 9

10

6.

5.

5. ___ + ___ − ___ = 10

6. ___ + ___ − ___ = 10

11

7.

8.

7. ___ + ___ − ___ = 11

8. ___ − ___ + ___ = 11

ADDITION AND SUBTRACTION

Look at the blank squares below. Then look at the block of numbers. Find three numbers in the same position that fit into the blanks in the number sentence to equal the target number.

4	0	3	3	8	4	2	4	7	7	5
7	8	8	0	5	3	6	2	7	2	4
7	2	0	5	3	0	2	9	6	8	0
6	7	1	5	8	6	0	9	7	9	4
7	9	8	9	1	9	2	4	0	9	0

(7)

1.

2.

1. ___ + ___ − ___ = 7

2. ___ − ___ + ___ = 7

(8)

3.

4.

3. ___ + ___ − ___ = 8

4. ___ − ___ + ___ = 8

(9)

5.

6.

5. ___ + ___ − ___ = 9

6. ___ + ___ − ___ = 9

(10)

7.

8.

7. ___ + ___ − ___ = 10

8. ___ − ___ + ___ = 10

Multiplication and Division

MULTIPLICATION AND DIVISION

Circle two numbers in touching squares whose product is 12. Find all you can. The numbers can be horizontal or vertical.

		3	7	8	4	3	
5	6	6	1	12	6	9	3
2	2					4	
			12			12	1
4	2					0	3
6	12	15			1		4
1	2	7	3	0	16	4	
2	6	5	12	1		2	

MULTIPLICATION AND DIVISION

Circle two numbers in touching squares whose product is 16. Find all you can.
The numbers can be horizontal or vertical.

4		8	4	8	4	10	3
7	9	4	5	2	12	2	8
	4				16	1	24
4	4		16			0	8
	8	0				10	8
3	5	16			8	2	9
6	3	1	15	7	9	4	4
6		9		3	5		2

MULTIPLICATION AND DIVISION

Circle two numbers in touching squares whose product is 24. Find all you can. The numbers can be horizontal or vertical.

8	4	5			3	0	8
	6	6	7	4	8	24	7
3	12	2				12	3
4	1		**24**			2	9
0	17					8	6
24		3		5	7	2	
1	5	8	18	4	19	6	4
	12	3	2	10	20		

MULTIPLICATION AND DIVISION

Circle two numbers in touching squares whose product is 18. Find all you can.
The numbers can be horizontal or vertical.

2	10	5	3	1	3	2	7
7	18	0	6	9	3	6	8
12	9	2		18		3	9
7	4					9	2
3	6					15	3
21	1	9					3
6	2	2	4	16	2	1	18
10	3	15	4	2	3	9	0

MULTIPLICATION AND DIVISION

Circle two numbers in touching squares whose quotient is 2. Find all you can.
The numbers can be horizontal or vertical.

	6	4	4		6	8	
7	4	1	2	5	3	9	4
8	6	3				8	4
5	6		**2**			2	2
20	10					5	1
2	1					10	14
0	4	2	5		9	18	7
6		1	4	6	3	16	4

MULTIPLICATION AND DIVISION

Circle two numbers in touching squares whose quotient is 3. Find all you can.
The numbers can be horizontal or vertical.

18	6	4	9	15	12		
9	3	1	3	5	21	7	36
	33	11				12	4
	5		**3**			6	18
9	3					2	
0	2					8	
4	12	3	18		18	10	30
36	6	1	24	8	9	27	

MULTIPLICATION AND DIVISION

Circle two numbers in touching squares whose quotient is 4. Find all you can. The numbers can be horizontal or vertical.

3	15	5	1	0	2	1	4
10	5	0	4	6	12	3	12
4	20					8	6
36	4		4			12	2
9	28					3	12
24	7					2	8
8	1	4	6	24	8	3	4
4	0	16	12	6	16	0	1

MULTIPLICATION AND DIVISION

Circle two numbers in touching squares whose quotient is 6. Find all you can.
The numbers can be horizontal or vertical.

9	12	24	6	36	3	72	9
3	18	4	1		2	12	18
	9	45			0	6	2
8	54		**6**			3	15
16	6					18	9
6	1			4		6	24
6	8	54	8	21	3	18	4
42	7	3	48	7	6	3	9

MULTIPLICATION AND DIVISION

Place the three numbers in the blanks, in any order, to equal the target number.

1.

___ X ___ + ___ = ___

5.

___ X ___ + ___ = ___

2.

___ X ___ + ___ = ___

6.

___ X ___ − ___ = ___

3.

___ X ___ − ___ = ___

7.

___ X ___ − ___ = ___

4.

___ X ___ + ___ = ___

8.

___ X ___ − ___ = ___

MULTIPLICATION AND DIVISION

Place the three numbers in the blanks, in any order, to equal the target number.

1.

___ X ___ + ___ = ___

2.

___ X ___ + ___ = ___

3.

___ X ___ − ___ = ___

4.

___ X ___ + ___ = ___

5.

___ X ___ + ___ = ___

6.

___ X ___ − ___ = ___

7.

___ X ___ − ___ = ___

8.

___ X ___ − ___ = ___

MULTIPLICATION AND DIVISION

Place the three numbers in the blanks, in any order, to equal the target number.

1.

___ x ___ + ___ = ___

2.

___ x ___ + ___ = ___

3.

___ x ___ − ___ = ___

4.

___ x ___ + ___ = ___

5.

___ x ___ + ___ = ___

6.

___ x ___ − ___ = ___

7.

___ x ___ − ___ = ___

8.

___ x ___ − ___ = ___

MULTIPLICATION AND DIVISION

Place the three numbers in the blanks, in any order, to equal the target number.

1.

___ X ___ + ___ = ___

2.

___ X ___ + ___ = ___

3.

___ X ___ – ___ = ___

4.

___ X ___ + ___ = ___

5.

___ X ___ + ___ = ___

6.

___ X ___ – ___ = ___

7.

___ X ___ – ___ = ___

8.

___ X ___ – ___ = ___

MULTIPLICATION AND DIVISION

Place the three numbers in the blanks, in any order, to equal the target number.

1.
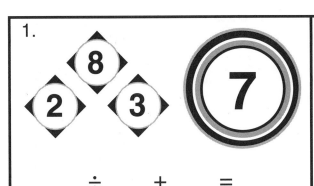

___ ÷ ___ + ___ = ___

2.
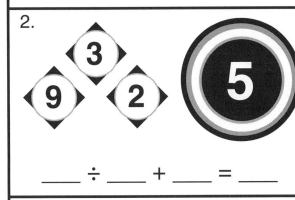

___ ÷ ___ + ___ = ___

3.

___ ÷ ___ − ___ = ___

4.

___ ÷ ___ + ___ = ___

5.

___ ÷ ___ + ___ = ___

6.

___ ÷ ___ − ___ = ___

7.

___ ÷ ___ − ___ = ___

8.

___ ÷ ___ − ___ = ___

MULTIPLICATION AND DIVISION

Place the three numbers in the blanks, in any order, to equal the target number.

1.
4 8 2 → 8

___ ÷ ___ + ___ = ___

5.
4 8 2 → 10

___ ÷ ___ + ___ = ___

2.
4 8 2 → 4

___ ÷ ___ + ___ = ___

6.
4 8 2 → 0

___ ÷ ___ − ___ = ___

3.
1 21 7 → 14

___ ÷ ___ − ___ = ___

7.
2 16 4 → 4

___ ÷ ___ − ___ = ___

4.
9 27 3 → 6

___ ÷ ___ + ___ = ___

8.
8 16 2 → 0

___ ÷ ___ − ___ = ___

MULTIPLICATION AND DIVISION

Place the three numbers in the blanks, in any order, to equal the target number.

1.

_____ ÷ _____ + _____ = _____

2.

_____ ÷ _____ + _____ = _____

3.
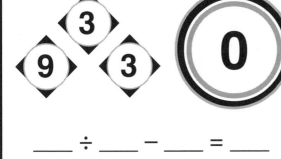

_____ ÷ _____ − _____ = _____

4.

_____ ÷ _____ + _____ = _____

5.

_____ ÷ _____ + _____ = _____

6.

_____ ÷ _____ − _____ = _____

7.

_____ ÷ _____ − _____ = _____

8.

_____ ÷ _____ − _____ = _____

MULTIPLICATION AND DIVISION

Place the three numbers in the blanks, in any order, to equal the target number.

1.

___ ÷ ___ + ___ = ___

2.
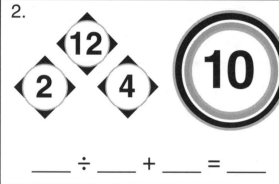

___ ÷ ___ + ___ = ___

3.

___ ÷ ___ − ___ = ___

4.
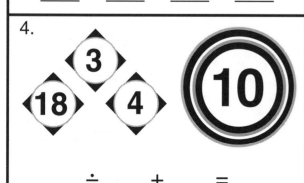

___ ÷ ___ + ___ = ___

5.
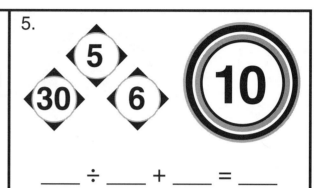

___ ÷ ___ + ___ = ___

6.

___ ÷ ___ − ___ = ___

7.

___ ÷ ___ − ___ = ___

8.

___ ÷ ___ − ___ = ___

MULTIPLICATION AND DIVISION

Place three of the four numbers in the blanks, in any order, to equal the target number.

1.

___ X ___ + ___ = ___

5.

___ X ___ − ___ = ___

2.

___ X ___ + ___ = ___

6.

___ X ___ − ___ = ___

3.

___ X ___ − ___ = ___

7.

___ X ___ + ___ = ___

4.

___ X ___ + ___ = ___

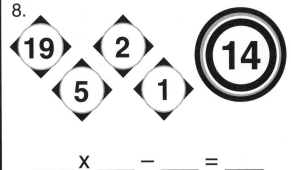

8.

___ X ___ − ___ = ___

MULTIPLICATION AND DIVISION

Place three of the four numbers in the blanks, in any order, to equal the target number.

1.
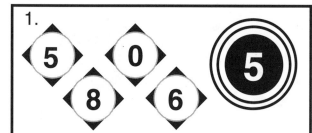

___ x ___ + ___ = ___

2.
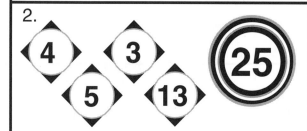

___ x ___ + ___ = ___

3.

___ x ___ – ___ = ___

4.

___ x ___ + ___ = ___

5.

___ x ___ – ___ = ___

6.

___ x ___ – ___ = ___

7.

___ x ___ + ___ = ___

8.

___ x ___ – ___ = ___

MULTIPLICATION AND DIVISION

Place three of the four numbers in the blanks, in any order, to equal the target number.

1.

___ x ___ + ___ = ___

5.

___ x ___ − ___ = ___

2.
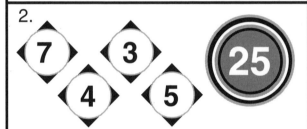

___ x ___ + ___ = ___

6.

___ x ___ − ___ = ___

3.
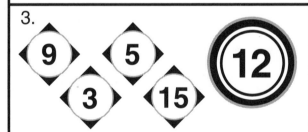

___ x ___ − ___ = ___

7.

___ x ___ + ___ = ___

4.

___ x ___ + ___ = ___

8.

___ x ___ − ___ = ___

MULTIPLICATION AND DIVISION

Place three of the four numbers in the blanks, in any order, to equal the target number.

1.

___ X ___ + ___ = ___

2.

___ X ___ + ___ = ___

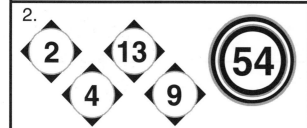

3.

___ X ___ − ___ = ___

4.

___ X ___ + ___ = ___

5.

___ X ___ − ___ = ___

6.

___ X ___ − ___ = ___

7.

___ X ___ + ___ = ___

8.

___ X ___ − ___ = ___

MULTIPLICATION AND DIVISION

Place three of the four numbers in the blanks, in any order, to equal the target number.

1.

____ ÷ ____ + ____ = ____

5.

____ ÷ ____ − ____ = ____

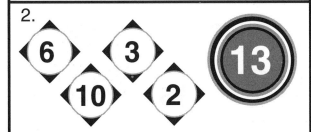

2.

____ ÷ ____ + ____ = ____

6.

____ ÷ ____ − ____ = ____

3.

____ ÷ ____ − ____ = ____

7.

____ ÷ ____ + ____ = ____

4.

____ ÷ ____ + ____ = ____

8.

____ ÷ ____ − ____ = ____

MULTIPLICATION AND DIVISION

Place three of the four numbers in the blanks, in any order, to equal the target number.

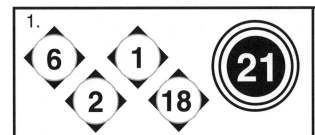

1.

____ ÷ ____ + ____ = ____

5.

____ ÷ ____ − ____ = ____

2.

____ ÷ ____ + ____ = ____

6.

____ ÷ ____ − ____ = ____

3.

____ ÷ ____ − ____ = ____

7.

____ ÷ ____ + ____ = ____

4.

____ ÷ ____ + ____ = ____

8.

____ ÷ ____ − ____ = ____

MULTIPLICATION AND DIVISION

Place three of the four numbers in the blanks, in any order, to equal the target number.

1.

___ ÷ ___ + ___ = ___

5.

___ ÷ ___ − ___ = ___

2.

___ ÷ ___ + ___ = ___

6.

___ ÷ ___ − ___ = ___

3.

___ ÷ ___ − ___ = ___

7.

___ ÷ ___ + ___ = ___

4.

___ ÷ ___ + ___ = ___

8.

___ ÷ ___ − ___ = ___

MULTIPLICATION AND DIVISION

Place three of the four numbers in the blanks, in any order, to equal the target number.

1.
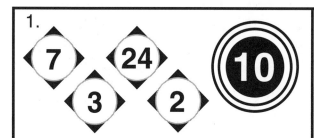

___ ÷ ___ + ___ = ___

5.

___ ÷ ___ − ___ = ___

2.

___ ÷ ___ + ___ = ___

6.

___ ÷ ___ − ___ = ___

3.

___ ÷ ___ − ___ = ___

7.

___ ÷ ___ + ___ = ___

4.

___ ÷ ___ + ___ = ___

8.
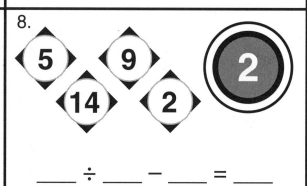

___ ÷ ___ − ___ = ___

Parentheses
and
Strategies

Parentheses say
"Do Me First"

$$(4 \times 5) - 1 = 19$$

$$4 \times (5 - 1) = 16$$

Place parentheses to make these sentences true:

$3 + 3 \times 2 = 12$	$3 + 3 \times 2 = 9$
$8 \div 2 - 1 = 8$	$8 \div 2 - 1 = 3$
$15 - 7 - 2 = 6$	$15 - 7 - 2 = 10$

PARENTHESES AND STRATEGIES

Insert parentheses to make each number sentence true. Remember, what's inside parentheses is done first.

1.
$8 - 6 \times 7 = 14$

5.
$9 \times 6 + 4 = 90$

2.
$5 + 2 \times 6 = 17$

6.
$4 \times 9 - 6 = 12$

3.
$5 + 6 \times 2 = 22$

7.
$9 - 8 \times 3 = 3$

4.
$9 - 6 \div 2 = 6$

8.
$8 \times 3 + 1 = 32$

PARENTHESES AND STRATEGIES

Insert parentheses to make each number sentence true. Remember, what's inside parentheses is done first.

1.

$$5 + 4 \div 3 = 3$$

2.

$$5 + 3 \div 4 = 2$$

3.

$$9 - 6 - 2 = 5$$

4.

$$9 - 6 + 2 = 5$$

5.

$$4 \div 5 - 3 = 2$$

6.

$$5 - 8 \div 2 = 1$$

7.
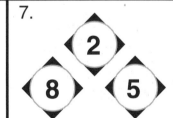

$$5 + 8 \times 2 = 21$$

8.

$$6 + 8 \div 2 = 7$$

PARENTHESES AND STRATEGIES

Insert parentheses to make each number sentence true. Remember, what's inside parentheses is done first.

1.

$6 - 3 \times 8 = 24$

2.
$8 \times 6 + 3 = 72$

3.
$4 - 2 \times 5 = 10$

4.

$2 - 5 - 4 = 1$

5.

$6 \times 8 - 3 = 30$

6.

$8 - 6 \times 3 = 6$

7.

$5 - 4 - 2 = 3$

8.

$2 + 5 \times 4 = 22$

Using Special Properties of 0 and 1 (Identity Elements)

Use each number once, in any order, to form a number sentence equaling the target number.

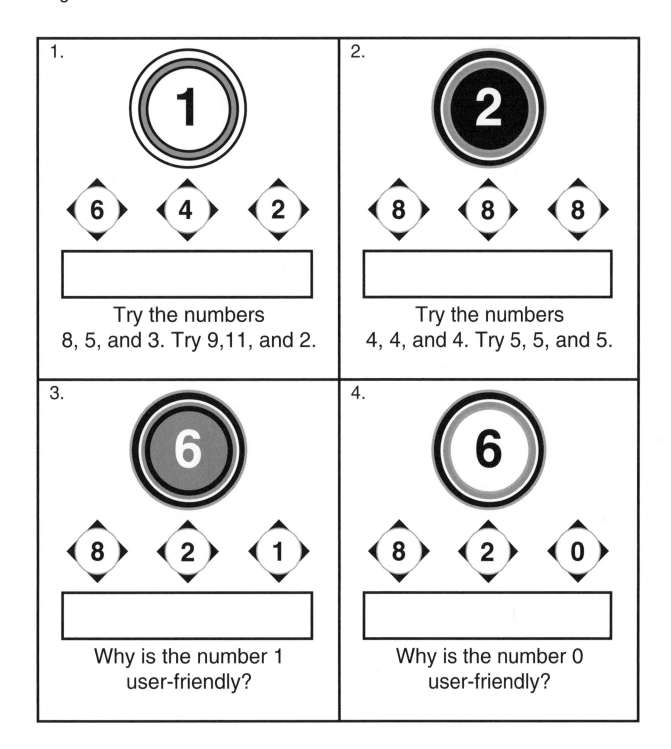

1.

1

6   4   2

Try the numbers
8, 5, and 3. Try 9,11, and 2.

2.

2

8   8   8

Try the numbers
4, 4, and 4. Try 5, 5, and 5.

3.

6

8   2   1

Why is the number 1
user-friendly?

4.

6

8   2   0

Why is the number 0
user-friendly?

Using Special Properties of 0 and 1 (Identity Elements)

Use each number once, in any order, to form a number sentence equaling the target number.

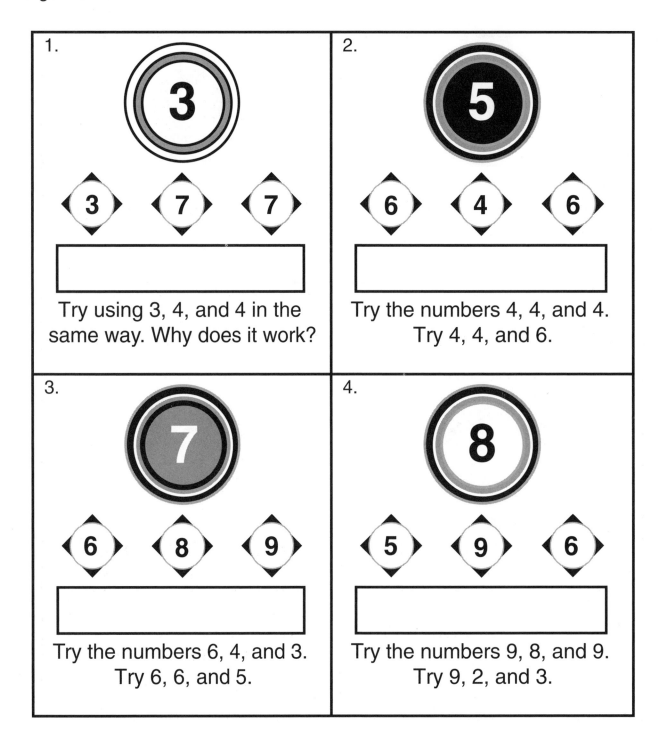

1.

3

3   7   7

Try using 3, 4, and 4 in the same way. Why does it work?

2.

5

6   4   6

Try the numbers 4, 4, and 4.
Try 4, 4, and 6.

3.

7

6   8   9

Try the numbers 6, 4, and 3.
Try 6, 6, and 5.

4.

8

5   9   6

Try the numbers 9, 8, and 9.
Try 9, 2, and 3.

PARENTHESES AND STRATEGIES

Identity Elements

Use the three numbers, in any order, to form a number sentence equaling the target number. Use parentheses to show what should be done first.

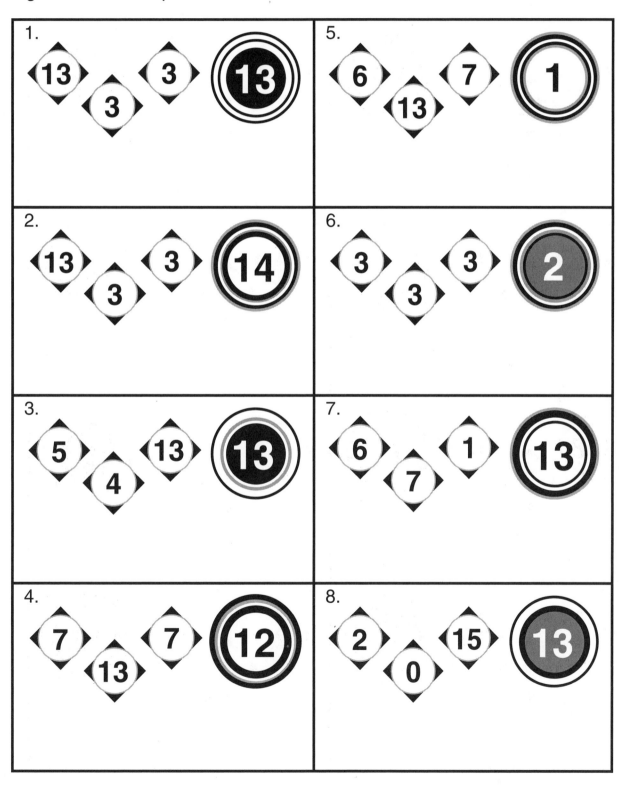

PARENTHESES AND STRATEGIES

Identity Elements

Use the three numbers, in any order, to form a number sentence equaling the target number. Use parentheses to show what should be done first.

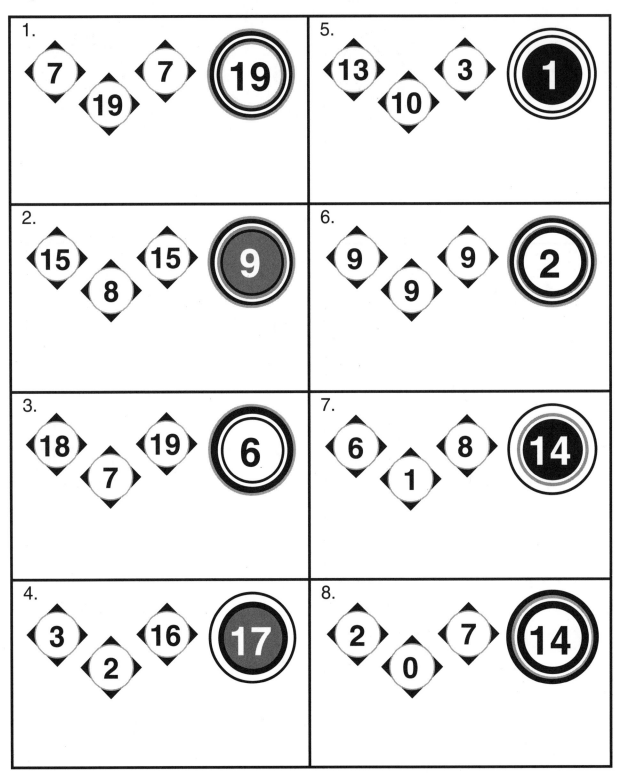

PARENTHESES AND STRATEGIES

Use each of the numbers once, in any order, to form number sentences equaling the two target numbers. Use parentheses to show what should be done first.

11 **12**

9 5 3

1. [ ] = 11
2. [ ] = 12

3 **20**

4 7 8

3. [ ] = 3
4. [ ] = 20

3 **20**

6 2 7

5. [ ] = 3
6. [ ] = 20

1 **15**

5 2 6

7. [ ] = 1
8. [ ] =15

PARENTHESES AND STRATEGIES

Use each of the numbers once, in any order, to form number sentences equaling the two target numbers. Use parentheses to show what should be done first.

9 **1**
8 **2** **7**

1. [_____] = 9

2. [_____] = 1

25 **0**
3 **4** **7**

3. [_____] = 25

4. [_____] = 0

20 **0**
4 **5** **0**

5. [_____] = 20

6. [_____] = 0

12 **4**
6 **3** **6**

7. [_____] = 12

8. [_____] = 4

PARENTHESES AND STRATEGIES

Use each of the numbers once, in any order, to form number sentences equaling the two target numbers. Use parentheses to show what should be done first.

6 **4**

4 3 8

1. [_____] = 6

2. [_____] = 4

8 **0**

5 2 2

3. [_____] = 8

4. [_____] = 0

14 **5**

2 7 4

5. [_____] =14

6. [_____] = 5

20 **25**

5 1 4

7. [_____] = 20

8. [_____] = 25

PARENTHESES AND STRATEGIES

Use each of the numbers once, in any order, to form number sentences equaling the two target numbers. Use parentheses to show what should be done first.

60 **19**

3 **4** **5**

1. [_____] = 60

2. [_____] = 19

12 **3**

6 **4** **8**

3. [_____] =12

4. [_____] = 3

4 **54**

9 **5** **9**

5. [_____] = 4

6. [_____] = 54

21 **1**

3 **7** **9**

7. [_____] = 21

8. [_____] = 1

PARENTHESES AND STRATEGIES

Find three connected numbers to use in an equation that equals the target number. Circle the three numbers and write a number sentence. Use parentheses to show what should be done first.

7	2	3	4	2	0	3	7	9	1	6
7	3	1	8	3	8	0	8	6	1	4
3	6	1	6	9	4	7	9	2	7	5
6	4	0	6	(8	4	1)	6	8	3	3
5	3	6	8	3	9	1	2	1	7	6

1. $(8 \div 4) - 1 = 1$

2. _____

3. _____

4. _____

5. _____

6. _____

7. _____

8. _____

PARENTHESES AND STRATEGIES

Find three connected numbers to use in an equation that equals the target number. Circle the three numbers and write a number sentence. Use parentheses to show what should be done first.

4	4	8	0	1	6	3	2	3	1	2
1	9	3	5	8	8	2	0	7	7	1
0	7	2	3	3	9	7	1	3	0	2
6	3	1	4	2	6	0	8	2	1	9
4	7	9	7	5	4	0	6	8	8	3

(5)

1. _____

2. _____

(6)

3. _____

4. _____

(7)

5. _____

6. _____

(8)

7. _____

8. _____

PARENTHESES AND STRATEGIES

Find three connected numbers to use in an equation that equals the target number. Circle the three numbers and write a number sentence. Use parentheses to show what should be done first.

8	2	9	3	3	5	3	6	3	8	9
7	7	5	1	2	1	8	7	3	1	2
6	9	3	3	2	8	3	2	9	8	2
1	9	5	9	5	3	1	4	4	4	1
6	4	5	3	0	6	5	6	7	8	4

9

1. _____

2. _____

10

3. _____

4. _____

11

5. _____

6. _____

12

7. _____

8. _____

PARENTHESES AND STRATEGIES

Find three connected numbers to use in an equation that equals the target number. Circle the three numbers and write a number sentence. Use parentheses to show what should be done first.

4	1	6	4	5	8	3	0	6	5	6
7	8	9	9	4	6	2	5	9	1	4
1	2	9	5	2	1	8	5	4	1	9
2	5	0	3	5	1	6	4	8	8	7
3	2	0	2	7	3	1	9	5	8	0

13

1. _____

2. _____

14

3. _____

4. _____

15

5. _____

6. _____

16

7. _____

8. _____

PARENTHESES AND STRATEGIES

Use three of the four numbers, in any order, to write a number sentence equaling the target number. Use parentheses to show what should be done first.

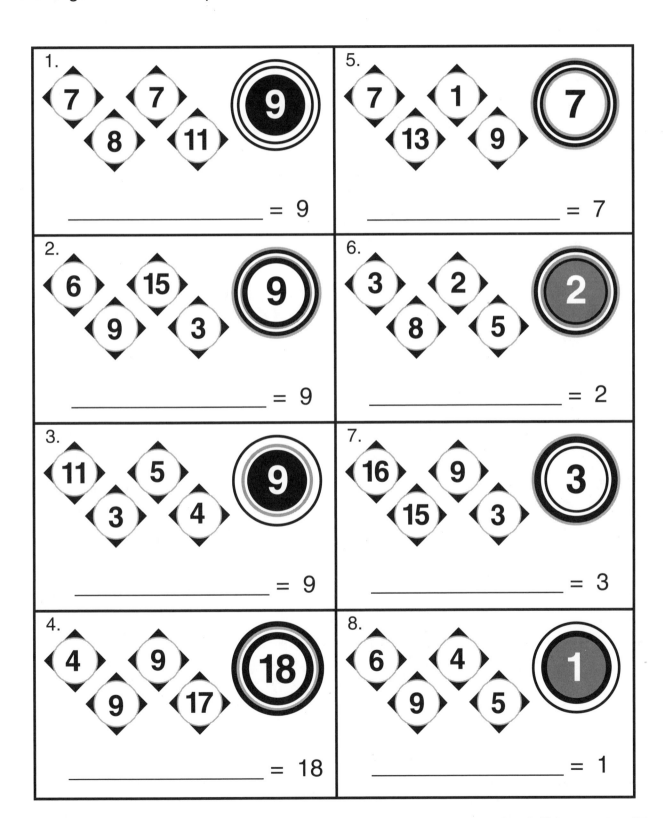

1. 7 7 8 11 ⬤9

_____ = 9

2. 6 15 9 3 ◯9

_____ = 9

3. 11 5 3 4 ⬤9

_____ = 9

4. 4 9 9 17 ◯18

_____ = 18

5. 7 1 13 9 ◯7

_____ = 7

6. 3 2 8 5 ⬤2

_____ = 2

7. 16 9 15 3 ◯3

_____ = 3

8. 6 4 9 5 ⬤1

_____ = 1

PARENTHESES AND STRATEGIES

Use three of the four numbers, in any order, to write a number sentence equaling the target number. Use parentheses to show what should be done first.

1.

_____ = 1

5.

_____ = 0

2.

_____ = 8

6.

_____ = 12

3.
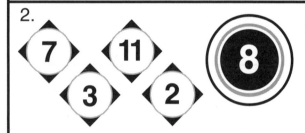
_____ = 18

7.

_____ = 36

4.

_____ = 16

8.

_____ = 9

PARENTHESES AND STRATEGIES

Use three of the four numbers, in any order, to write a number sentence equaling the target number. Use parentheses to show what should be done first.

1.

_____ = 0

2.

_____ = 12

3.

_____ = 27

4.

_____ = 4

5.

_____ = 11

6.

_____ = 2

7.

_____ = 10

8.

_____ = 6

PARENTHESES AND STRATEGIES

Use three of the four numbers, in any order, to write a number sentence equaling the target number. Use parentheses to show what should be done first.

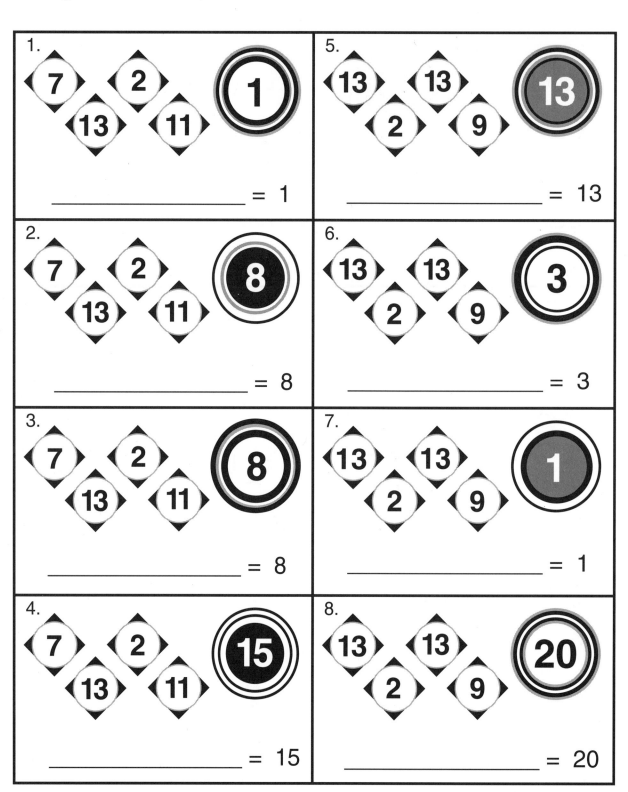

1.

7 2 13 11

_____ = 1

2.

7 2 13 11

_____ = 8

3.

7 2 13 11

_____ = 8

4.

7 2 13 11

_____ = 15

5.

13 13 2 9

_____ = 13

6.

13 13 2 9

_____ = 3

7.

13 13 2 9

_____ = 1

8.

13 13 2 9

_____ = 20

PARENTHESES AND STRATEGIES

Look at the blank squares below. Then look at the block of numbers. Find three numbers in the same position that fit into the blanks in the number sentence to equal the target number.

9	6	1	8	2	8	9	4	2	1	2
4	4	5	3	3	7	8	5	2	9	2
8	2	4	0	6	3	9	2	0	2	1
2	5	0	1	6	2	7	8	2	3	3
7	4	3	5	1	5	0	9	6	4	1

10

1.

2.

1. ___ + ___ − ___ = ___

2. ___ x ___ + ___ = ___

9

3.

4.

3. ___ ÷ ___ + ___ = ___

4. ___ − ___ + ___ = ___

11

5.

6.

5. ___ x ___ − ___ = ___

6. ___ ÷ ___ + ___ = ___

9

7.

8.

7. ___ + ___ − ___ = ___

8. ___ x ___ ÷ ___ = ___

PARENTHESES AND STRATEGIES

Look at the blank squares below. Then look at the block of numbers. Find three numbers in the same position that fit into the blanks in the number sentence to equal the target number.

8	2	1	9	1	2	0	4	7	3	8
2	1	3	3	7	4	8	6	3	6	4
4	3	7	6	2	2	2	6	5	1	7
1	8	2	7	6	5	1	5	1	9	2
0	5	4	0	5	9	0	9	5	2	3

(5)

1.   2.

1. ___ + ___ − ___ = ___

2. ___ x ___ + ___ = ___

(10)

3.   4.

3. ___ ÷ ___ + ___ = ___

4. ___ − ___ + ___ = ___

(10)

6.

5.

5. ___ x ___ − ___ = ___

6. ___ ÷ ___ + ___ = ___

(10)

7.   8.

7. ___ + ___ − ___ = ___

8. ___ x ___ ÷ ___ = ___

PARENTHESES AND STRATEGIES

Look at the blank squares below. Then look at the block of numbers. Find three numbers in the same position that fit into the blanks in the number sentence to equal the target number.

3	2	0	8	6	1	9	7	9	1	2
9	8	1	2	4	2	0	7	8	3	5
1	2	6	7	4	2	5	5	2	7	8
9	6	3	3	9	0	8	1	8	0	2
4	5	6	1	4	5	7	3	2	6	9

(10)

1.   2.

1. ___ + ___ − ___ = ___

2. ___ x ___ + ___ = ___

(11)

3.   4.

3. ___ ÷ ___ + ___ = ___

4. ___ − ___ + ___ = ___

(13)

5.   6.

5. ___ x ___ − ___ = ___

6. ___ ÷ ___ + ___ = ___

(12)

7.   8.

7. ___ + ___ − ___ = ___

8. ___ x ___ ÷ ___ = ___

PARENTHESES AND STRATEGIES

Look at the blank squares below. Then look at the block of numbers. Find three numbers in the same position that fit into the blanks in the number sentence to equal the target number.

6	1	4	3	8	4	5	3	3	9	8
2	3	5	9	5	8	9	2	3	2	0
1	3	7	3	1	0	1	2	7	6	3
0	8	5	7	2	7	5	5	9	6	4
5	3	6	8	5	7	6	3	1	1	4

⑦   1.   2.

1.
___ + ___ − ___ = ___

2.
___ x ___ + ___ = ___

⑥   3.   4.

3.
___ ÷ ___ + ___ = ___

4.
___ − ___ + ___ = ___

⑦   5.   6.

5.
___ x ___ − ___ = ___

6.
___ ÷ ___ + ___ = ___

⑧   7.   8.

7.
___ + ___ − ___ = ___

8.
___ x ___ ÷ ___ = ___

Order of Operations and Use of Parentheses

As students begin to solve more difficult problems, it may be important for them to understand the order of operations when writing out the solution to the problem. When a number sentence is written using two or more operation symbols (+,−,x,÷), its meaning may be ambiguous. For example, the number sentence 5 x 2 + 3 would equal 13 if the multiplication was performed first, but if the addition was done first, the answer would be 25. It is for this reason that a convention or agreement has been determined on which operations should take first preference. This convention is known as the order of operations.

The rule for the order of operations is as follows:

> **First do all multiplications and divisions in order from left to right. Then do all additions and subtractions in order from left to right.**

Millions of math students over the years have remembered this rule for determining the correct order of operations by using the phrase, **"My Dear Aunt Sally."** **M, D, A,** and **S**, the first letters of each word, stand for multiplication, division, addition, and subtraction. The phrase may be helpful, but one must be careful not to think that multiplication has any precedence over division—nor does addition have any precedence over subtraction.

The examples below show applications of the rules for the order of operations:

1. $5 \times 2 + 3 = (5 \times 2) + 3 + 10 + 3 = 13$
2. $5 + 2 \times 3 = 5 + (2 \times 3) = 5 + 6 = 11$
3. $12 \div 6 + 3 = (12 \div 6) + 3 = 2 + 3 = 5$
4. $12 + 6 \div 3 = 12 + (6 \div 3) = 12 + 2 = 14$
5. $12 \times 6 \div 3 = (12 \times 6) \div 3 = 72 \div 3 = 24$
6. $12 \div 6 \times 3 = (12 \div 6) \times 3 = 2 \times 3 = 6$
7. $10 - 9 \div 3 = 10 - (9 \div 3) = 10 - 3 = 7$
8. $11 + 8 \div 4 - 2 = 11 + (8 \div 4) - 2 = 11 + 2 - 2 = 11$
9. $48 \div 4 - 3 \times 2 = (48 \div 4) - (3 \times 2) = 12 - 6 = 6$
10. $12 + 8 - 6 \div 2 \times 1 = 12 + 8 - (6 \div 2) \times 1 =$
    $12 + 8 - (3 \times 1) = 12 + 8 - 3 = 20 - 3 = 17$

The worksheets on the order of operations will provide practice in applying the rule.

Use of Parentheses

The use of parentheses is another way to indicate the order of operations in a number sentence when two or more operation symbols are used. Parentheses group together two or more numbers that are to be simplified first. Parentheses take precedence over the rule for the order of operations. For example, in the number phrase 8 + 2 x 4 multiplication takes precedence over addition, so the phrase is simplified as 8 + 8, or 16. If, however, the number phrase were (8 + 2) x 4, then the parentheses would take precedence over multiplication and the phrase would be evaluated as 10 x 4, or 40.

In general, Target Practice™ puzzles are simple enough not to require students to have mastered the order of operations or use of parentheses. However, if some of the more advanced students want to solve problems involving four or five numbers, it may be advisable to introduce them to these concepts. Most students will prefer using parentheses to clarify their answers.

When several numbers are used in a number phrase or number sentence, it may be necessary to use more than one set of parentheses. When one set of parentheses lies within another, perform the operations within the innermost parentheses first. Sometimes when parentheses lie within each other, brackets ([ ]) and braces ({ }) are used to make clear which sets belong to each other: { [( )] }

Several examples of the simplification of number phrases involving parentheses are shown below. Worksheets on the order of operations and use of parentheses are provided on the next few pages.

1. $(7 + 9) \times 2 = 16 \times 2 = 32$
2. $7 + (9 \times 2) = 7 + 18 = 25$
3. $7 + 9 \times 2 = 7 + 18 = 25$
4. $12 - 3 \div 3 = 12 - (3 \div 3) = 12 - 1 = 11$
5. $(12 - 3) \div 3 = 9 \div 3 = 3$
6. $12 - (3 \div 3) = 12 - 1 = 11$
7. $(4 + 8) \times (7 - 5) = 12 \times 2 = 24$
8. $4 + 8 \times (7 - 5) = 4 + 8 \times 2 = 4 + (8 \times 2) = 4 + 16 = 20$
9. $4 + 8 \times 7 - 5 = 4 + (8 \times 7) - 5 = 4 + 56 - 5 = 60 - 5 = 55$
10. $[16 \div (4 + 4)] \times 3 = [16 \div 8] \times 3 = 2 \times 3 = 6$
11. $[(16 \div 4) + 4] \times 3 = [4 + 4] \times 3 = 8 \times 3 = 24$
12. $(16 \div 4) + (4 \times 3) = 4 + 12 = 16$
13. $16 \div [4 + (4 \times 3)] = 16 \div [4 + 12] = 16 \div 16 = 1$

Rule for the *order of operations*: first do all multiplications and divisions from left to right. Then do all additions and subtractions from left to right. Apply this rule to the problems below to find their values.

1. $8 + 2 \times 4 =$	11. $12 + 6 \times 2 =$
2. $8 \times 2 + 4 =$	12. $12 \times 6 + 2 =$
3. $8 \div 2 + 4 =$	13. $12 \div 6 + 2 =$
4. $8 + 2 \div 4 =$	14. $12 + 6 \div 2 =$
5. $8 \div 2 \times 4 =$	15. $12 \div 6 \times 2 =$
6. $8 \times 2 \div 4 =$	16. $12 \times 6 \div 2 =$
7. $8 - 2 + 4 =$	17. $12 - 6 + 2 =$
8. $8 + 2 - 4 =$	18. $12 + 6 - 2 =$
9. $8 - 2 \times 4 =$	19. $12 - 6 \times 2 =$
10. $8 \times 2 - 4 =$	20. $12 \times 6 - 2 =$

ORDER OF OPERATIONS

Rule for the *order of operations*: first do all multiplications and divisions from left to right. Then do all additions and subtractions from left to right. Apply this rule to the problems below to find their values.

1. $(8 + 2) \times (4 - 2) =$	13. $[8 \times (2 + 4)] \div 2 =$
2. $(8 + 2) - (4 \times 2) =$	14. $8 \times [2 \div (4 + 2)] =$
3. $(8 \div 2) + (4 \times 2) =$	15. $[8 + (2 \div 4)] \times 2 =$
4. $(8 \div 2) \times (4 + 2) =$	16. $(8 + 2) \times (4 \div 2) =$
5. $(8 - 2) \times (4 + 2) =$	17. $8 - (2 \div 4) \times 2 =$
6. $[(8 - 2) + 4] \times 2 =$	18. $8 - (2 \times 4) \div 2 =$
7. $8 \times [(2 - 4) \div 2] =$	19. $8 \div [2 - (4 \times 2)] =$
8. $[8 \times (2 \div 4)] - 2 =$	20. $[(8 \div 2) \times 4] - 2 =$
9. $[(8 \div 2) + 4] - 2 =$	21. $(8 + 2) \div (4 - 2) =$
10. $[(8 \div 2) - 4] + 2 =$	22. $8 + [(2 - 4) \div 2] =$
11. $[8 - (2 + 4)] \div 2 =$	23. $8 \times (2 + 4) - 2 =$
12. $8 - [2 \div (4 + 2)] =$	24. $8 \times [2 - (4 + 2)] =$

USE OF PARENTHESES

Perform the operations within parentheses first. Then find the value of the number phrase.

1. $12 + (4 \times 2) =$	11. $12 - (4 \div 2) =$
2. $(12 + 4) \times 2 =$	12. $(12 - 4) \div 2 =$
3. $12 \div (4 + 2) =$	13. $12 \times (4 + 2) =$
4. $(12 \div 4) + 2 =$	14. $(12 \times 4) + 2 =$
5. $12 - (4 \times 2) =$	15. $12 \div (4 \times 2) =$
6. $(12 - 4) \times 2 =$	16. $(12 \div 4) \times 2 =$
7. $12 \times (4 - 2) =$	17. $12 \times (4 \div 2) =$
8. $(12 \times 4) - 2 =$	18. $(12 \times 4) \div 2 =$
9. $12 + (4 - 2) =$	19. $12 \times (4 \times 2) =$
10. $(12 + 4) - 2 =$	20. $(12 \times 4) \times 2 =$

USE OF PARENTHESES

Perform the operations within parentheses first. Then find the value of the number phrase. (Remove the innermost parentheses first, then evaluate what's in the brackets.)

1. $(8 + 2) \times (4 - 2) =$	13. $[8 \times (2 + 4)] \div 2 =$
2. $(8 + 2) - (4 \times 2) =$	14. $8 \times [2 \div (4 + 2)] =$
3. $(8 \div 2) + (4 \times 2) =$	15. $[8 + (2 \div 4)] \times 2 =$
4. $(8 \div 2) \times (4 + 2) =$	16. $(8 + 2) \times (4 \div 2) =$
5. $(8 - 2) \times (4 + 2) =$	17. $8 - (2 \div 4) \times 2 =$
6. $[(8 - 2) + 4] \times 2 =$	18. $8 - (2 \times 4) \div 2 =$
7. $8 \times [(2 - 4) \div 2] =$	19. $8 \div [2 - (4 \times 2)] =$
8. $[8 \times (2 \div 4)] - 2 =$	20. $[(8 \div 2) \times 4] - 2 =$
9. $[(8 \div 2) + 4] - 2 =$	21. $(8 + 2) \div (4 - 2) =$
10. $[(8 \div 2) - 4] + 2 =$	22. $8 + [(2 - 4) \div 2] =$
11. $[8 - (2 + 4)] \div 2 =$	23. $8 \times (2 + 4) - 2 =$
12. $8 - [2 \div (4 + 2)] =$	24. $8 \times [2 - (4 + 2)] =$

92 • Target Practice™ Grades 1–5
Copyright © Dale Seymour Publications

Target Practice™ Formats and Random Digits

TARGET PRACTICE FORMAT

Circle two numbers in touching squares that add to _____. Find all you can. The numbers can be horizontal or vertical.

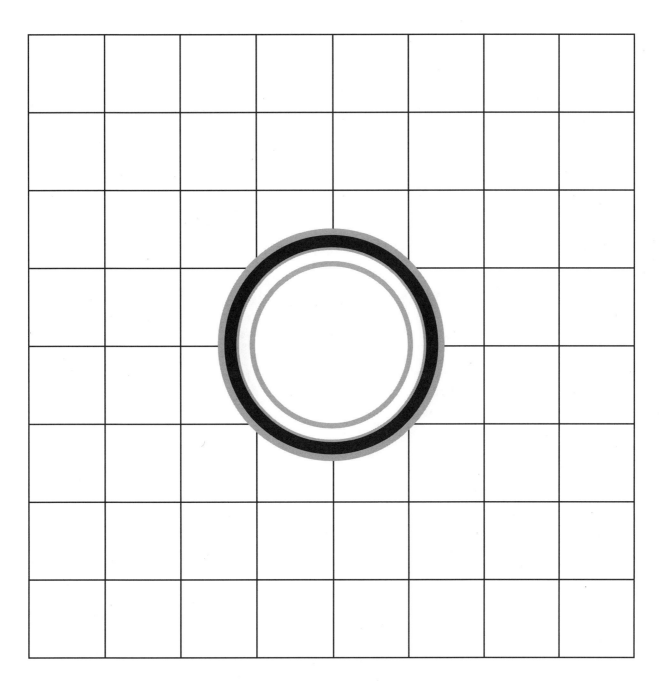

TARGET PRACTICE FORMAT

Circle two numbers in touching squares that add to   . Find all you can.
The numbers can be horizontal or vertical.

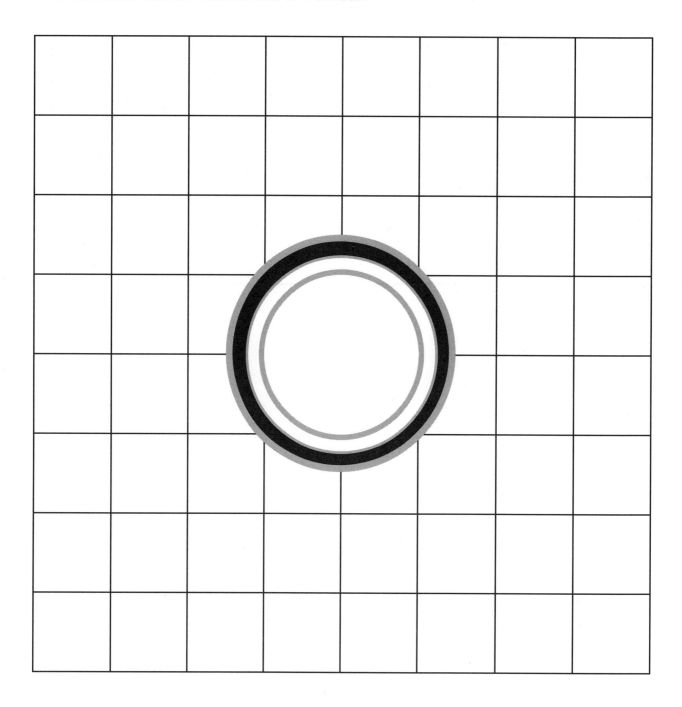

TARGET PRACTICE FORMAT

Circle three numbers in a line of touching squares that add to ___. Find all you can. The numbers can be horizontal or vertical.

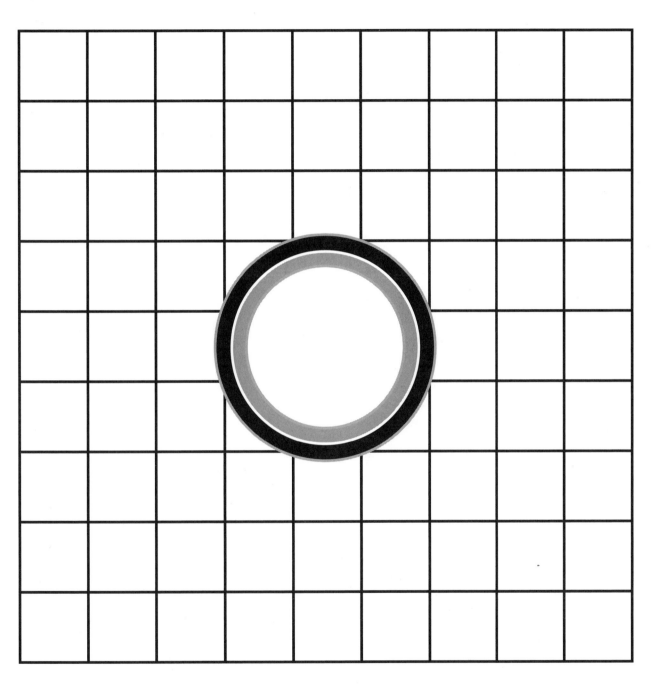

TARGET PRACTICE FORMAT

Place the three numbers in the blanks to equal the target number.

1.
___ + ___ − ___ = ___

2.
___ + ___ − ___ = ___

3.
___ + ___ − ___ = ___

4.
___ + ___ − ___ = ___

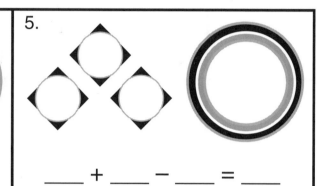

5.
___ + ___ − ___ = ___

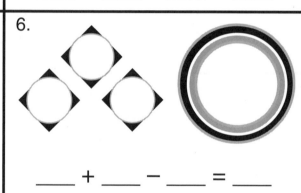

6.
___ + ___ − ___ = ___

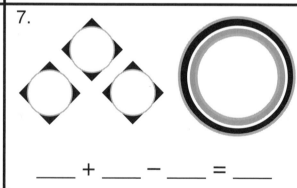

7.
___ + ___ − ___ = ___

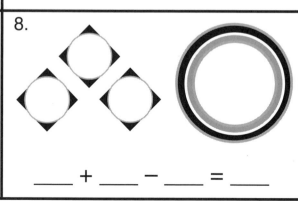

8.
___ + ___ − ___ = ___

TARGET PRACTICE FORMAT

Place the three numbers in the blanks to equal the target number.

1.
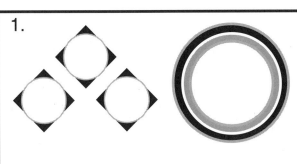

___ X ___ + ___ = ___

5.
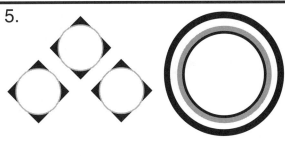

___ X ___ + ___ = ___

2.
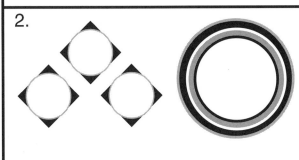

___ X ___ + ___ = ___

6.
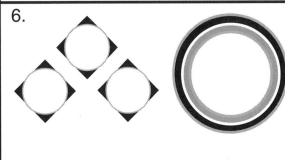
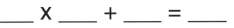

___ X ___ – ___ = ___

3.

___ X ___ – ___ = ___

7.

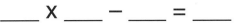

___ X ___ – ___ = ___

4.
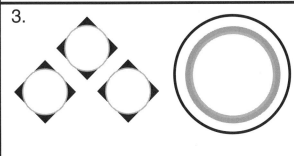

___ X ___ + ___ = ___

8.
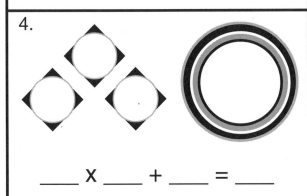
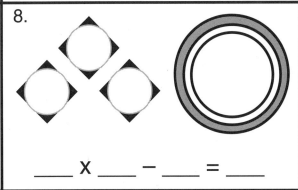

___ X ___ – ___ = ___

TARGET PRACTICE FORMAT

Use the three numbers, in any order, to write a number sentence equaling the target number. Use parentheses to show what should be done first.

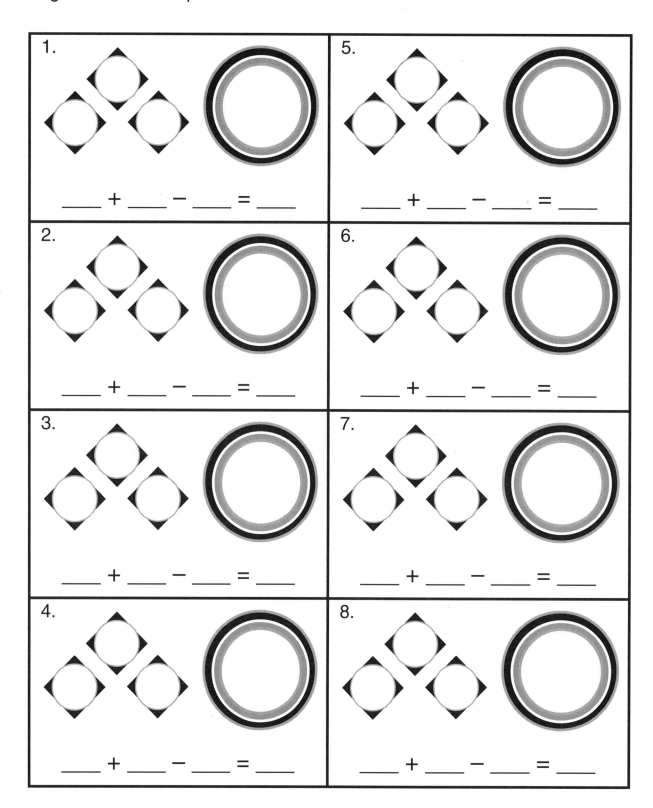

1. ___ + ___ − ___ = ___

2. ___ + ___ − ___ = ___

3. ___ + ___ − ___ = ___

4. ___ + ___ − ___ = ___

5. ___ + ___ − ___ = ___

6. ___ + ___ − ___ = ___

7. ___ + ___ − ___ = ___

8. ___ + ___ − ___ = ___

TARGET PRACTICE FORMAT

Circle four numbers in touching squares that add to _____. Find all you can. The numbers can be horizontal or vertical.

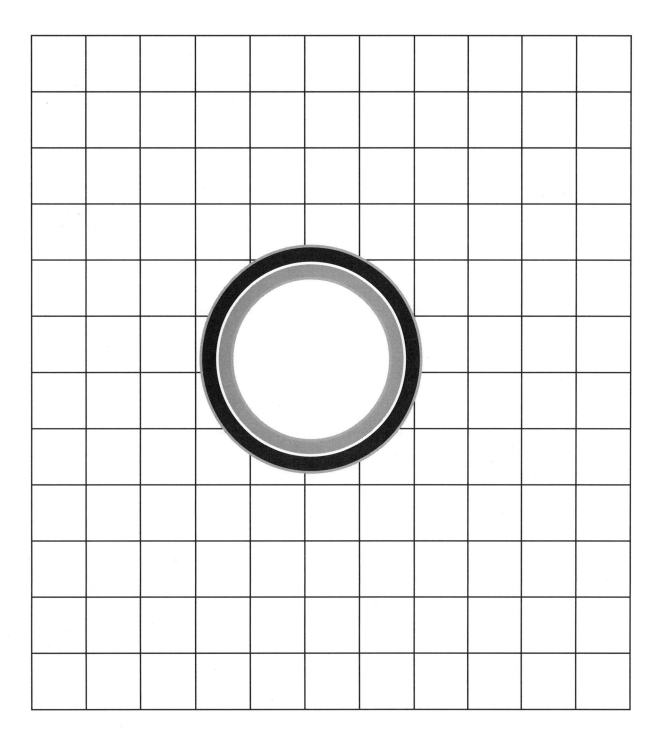

TARGET PRACTICE FORMAT

Look at the blank squares below. Then look at the block of numbers. Find three numbers in the same position that fit into the blanks in the number sentence to equal the target number.

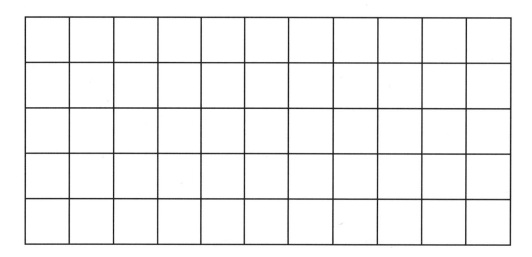

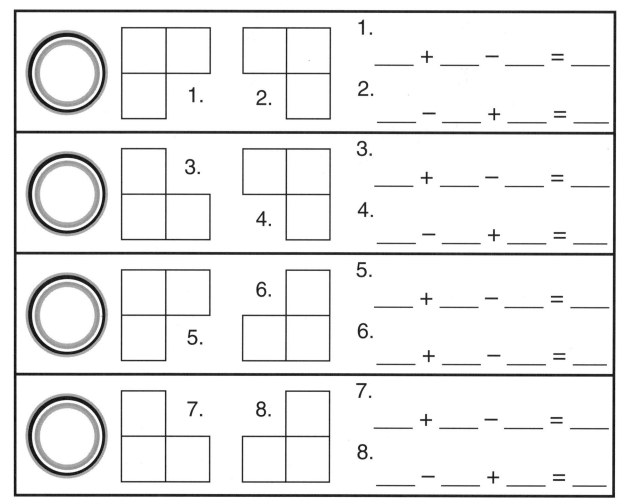

Circle two numbers in touching squares whose product is _____. Find all you can. The numbers can be horizontal or vertical.

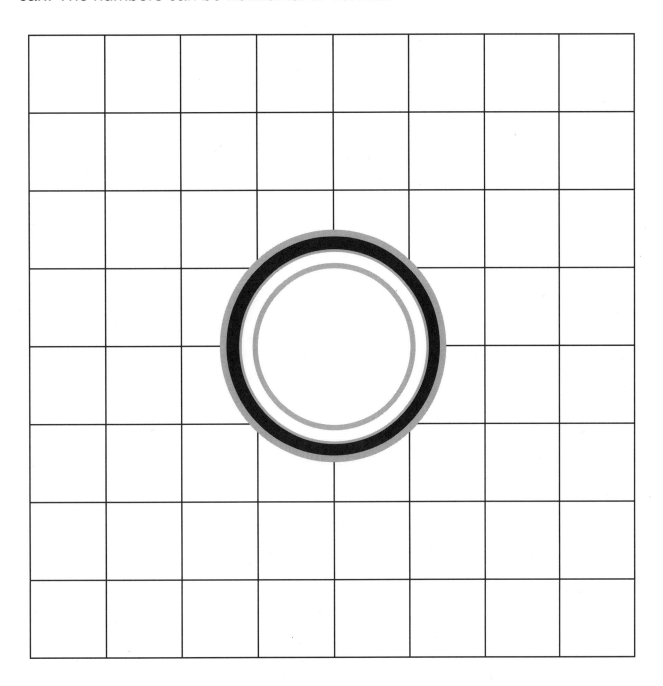

TARGET PRACTICE FORMAT

Circle two numbers in touching squares whose quotient is _____ . Find all you can. The numbers can be horizontal or vertical.

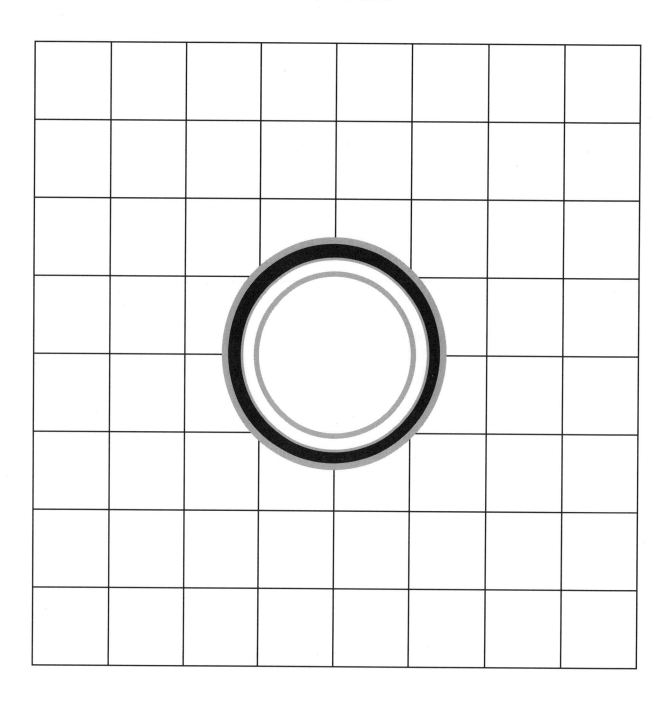

TARGET PRACTICE FORMAT

Place three of the four numbers in the blanks, in any order, to equal the target number.

1.
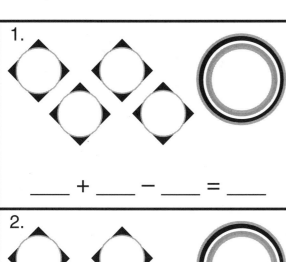

___ + ___ − ___ = ___

5.
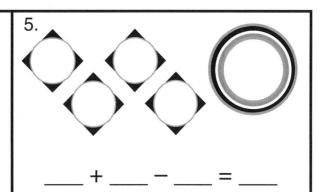

___ + ___ − ___ = ___

2.
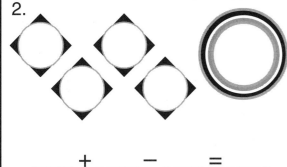

___ + ___ − ___ = ___

6.
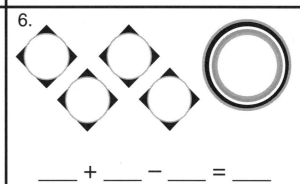

___ + ___ − ___ = ___

3.
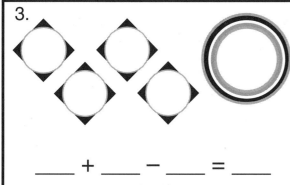

___ + ___ − ___ = ___

7.
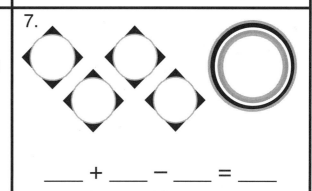

___ + ___ − ___ = ___

4.
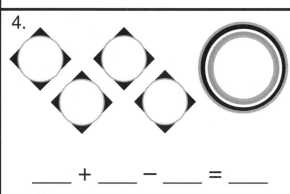

___ + ___ − ___ = ___

8.
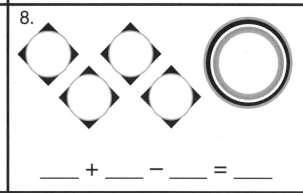

___ + ___ − ___ = ___

TARGET PRACTICE FORMAT

Use three of the four numbers, in any order, to write a number sentence equaling the target number.

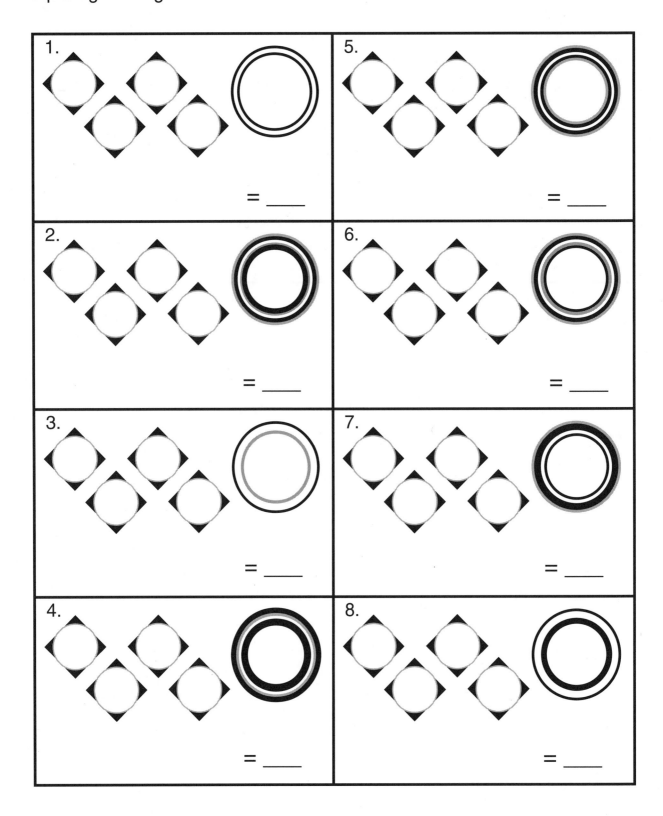

TARGET PRACTICE FORMAT

Look at the blank squares below. Then look at the block of numbers. Find three numbers in the same position that fit into the blanks in the number sentence to equal the target number.

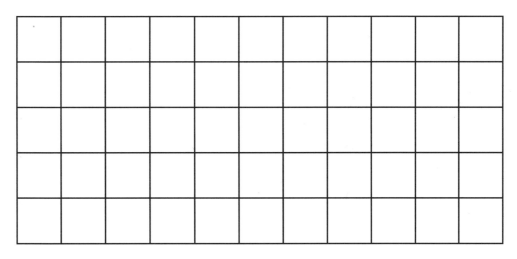

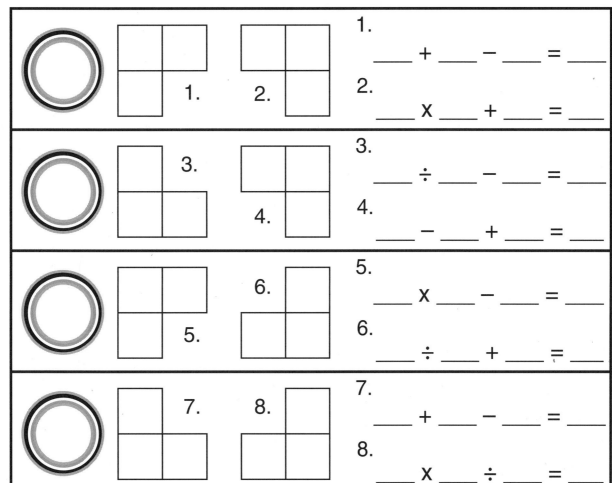

1. ___ + ___ − ___ = ___

2. ___ x ___ + ___ = ___

3. ___ ÷ ___ − ___ = ___

4. ___ − ___ + ___ = ___

5. ___ x ___ − ___ = ___

6. ___ ÷ ___ + ___ = ___

7. ___ + ___ − ___ = ___

8. ___ x ___ ÷ ___ = ___

TARGET PRACTICE FORMAT

Look at the blank squares below. Then look at the block of numbers. Find three numbers in the same position that fit into the blanks in the number sentence to equal the target number.

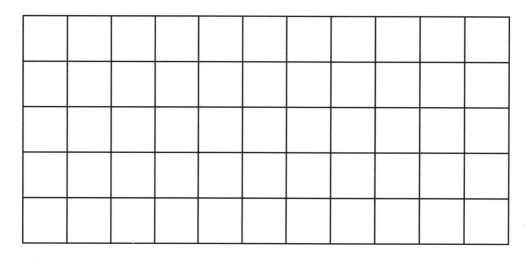

	1.	2.
⊙		

1.
2.

	3.	4.
⊙		

3.
4.

	5.	6.
⊙		

5.
6.

	7.	8.
⊙		

7.
8.

TARGET PRACTICE FORMAT

Find three connected numbers you can use in an equation that equals the target number. Circle the three numbers and write a number sentence. Use parentheses to show what should be done first.

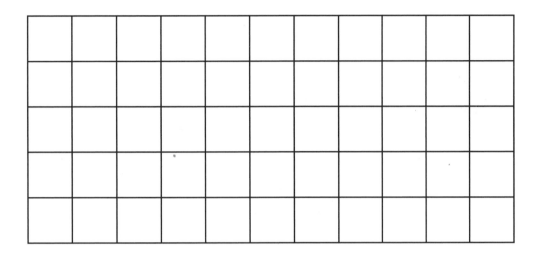

1. _____

2. _____

3. _____

4. _____

5. _____

6. _____

7. _____

8. _____

TARGET PRACTICE FORMAT

Use each of the numbers once, in any order, to form a number sentence equaling the target number.

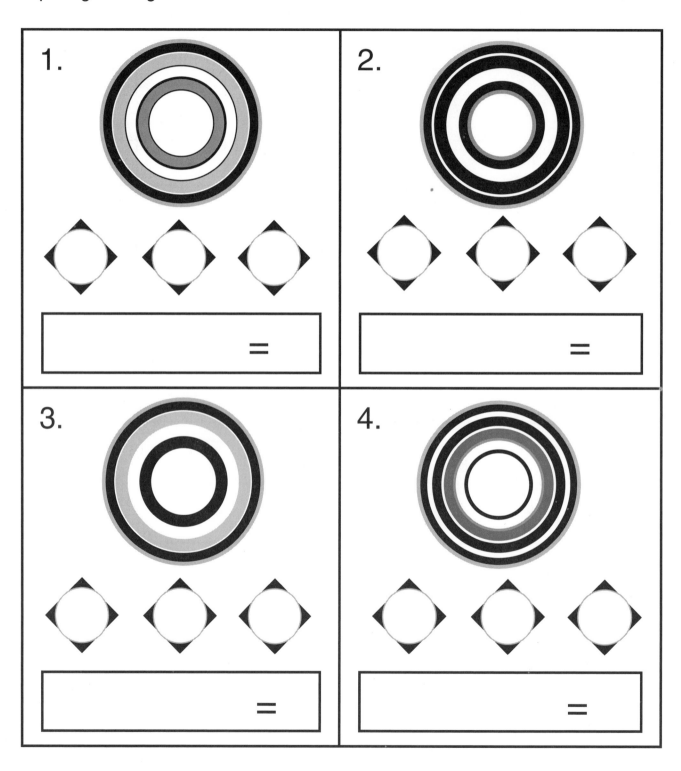

TARGET PRACTICE FORMAT

Use each of the numbers once, in any order, to form a number sentence equaling the target number.

1. _____ =

2. _____ =

3. _____ =

4. _____ =

5. _____ =

6. _____ =

7. _____ =

8. _____ =

4	9	4	8	7	5	2	8
2	9	4	8	0	9	1	5
2	5	2	5	2	9	7	7
0	2	4	3	1	4	2	1
6	9	4	1	4	8	9	3
7	7	2	8	5	3	5	1
5	2	6	5	2	6	6	0
9	8	7	4	0	9	8	0
8	5	0	2	2	5	8	7
1	6	3	4	6	0	1	6

RANDOM DIGITS

8	1	8	3	3	9	3	4
6	3	7	8	9	5	4	9
6	1	8	4	0	8	1	7
4	2	2	4	3	1	0	1
4	5	2	3	6	0	9	1
4	0	3	3	8	4	2	4
5	4	0	4	0	7	1	2
4	9	1	5	8	2	9	0
8	6	9	6	8	0	3	1
0	7	6	3	6	0	4	5

4	8	7	4	5	4	7	6
3	2	5	1	9	9	1	9
7	5	7	5	7	1	2	9
3	0	5	4	3	6	6	0
6	8	4	4	2	5	5	1
2	2	4	0	3	5	6	6
7	0	7	0	1	3	6	9
6	9	8	0	4	9	1	2
9	8	6	7	5	7	7	6
0	1	5	2	2	8	1	3

RANDOM DIGITS

4	8	7	4	5	4	7	6
3	2	5	1	9	9	1	9
7	5	7	5	7	1	2	9
3	0	5	4	3	6	6	0
6	8	4	4	2	5	5	1
2	2	4	0	3	5	6	6
7	0	7	0	1	3	6	9
6	9	8	0	4	9	1	2
9	8	6	7	5	7	7	6
0	1	5	2	2	8	1	3

RANDOM DIGITS

3	2	4	5	5	1	8	0	6	2	5	2
8	3	1	3	5	1	4	2	9	1	4	1
4	1	7	4	1	3	0	6	9	2	5	0
0	2	3	1	2	3	9	8	0	5	6	3
3	7	9	3	7	1	9	0	7	7	1	3
6	9	6	6	8	9	4	4	0	6	1	6
3	4	2	8	2	5	3	5	1	7	4	4
1	2	8	3	4	3	4	8	6	4	2	6
5	3	6	4	1	2	5	7	2	0	0	6
1	8	6	8	8	3	3	1	9	1	0	2
2	5	3	9	3	7	5	0	0	4	1	3
5	6	7	3	1	4	2	0	1	4	8	8
8	8	4	6	3	8	4	1	4	8	5	6
8	4	9	3	9	9	2	9	7	8	8	0
5	8	8	7	2	8	3	5	0	6	0	6

RANDOM DIGITS

4	1	7	4	2	6	5	7	3	1	2	5
8	6	8	8	4	1	8	6	6	3	8	1
7	2	2	5	2	4	9	3	8	3	9	4
6	4	8	8	7	3	2	0	5	7	3	1
9	5	8	0	6	8	3	8	0	6	3	4
0	3	4	0	3	4	2	0	6	7	6	4
1	5	5	1	4	5	0	7	6	3	3	7
4	4	8	0	1	3	1	2	1	8	2	0
7	1	0	7	2	3	3	7	1	6	3	1
0	8	9	4	7	9	7	5	4	0	6	8
3	3	5	3	6	8	3	9	1	2	1	7
6	9	8	3	8	2	1	9	5	3	1	4
4	1	6	4	5	3	0	6	5	6	7	8
9	9	4	2	5	9	1	4	1	2	9	5
2	8	5	4	1	9	2	5	0	3	5	1

Puzzle
Solutions

Answers May Vary

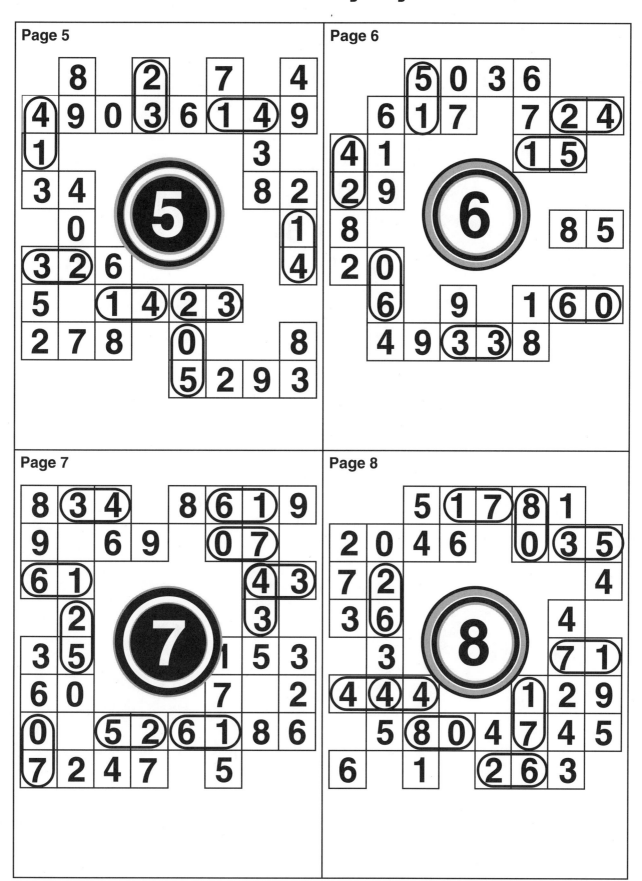

Answers May Vary

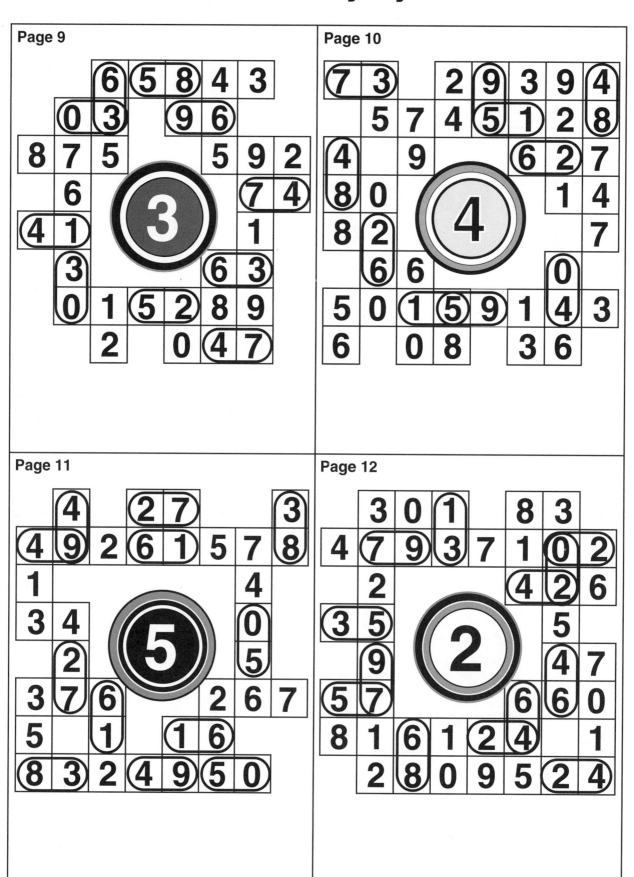

Answers May Vary

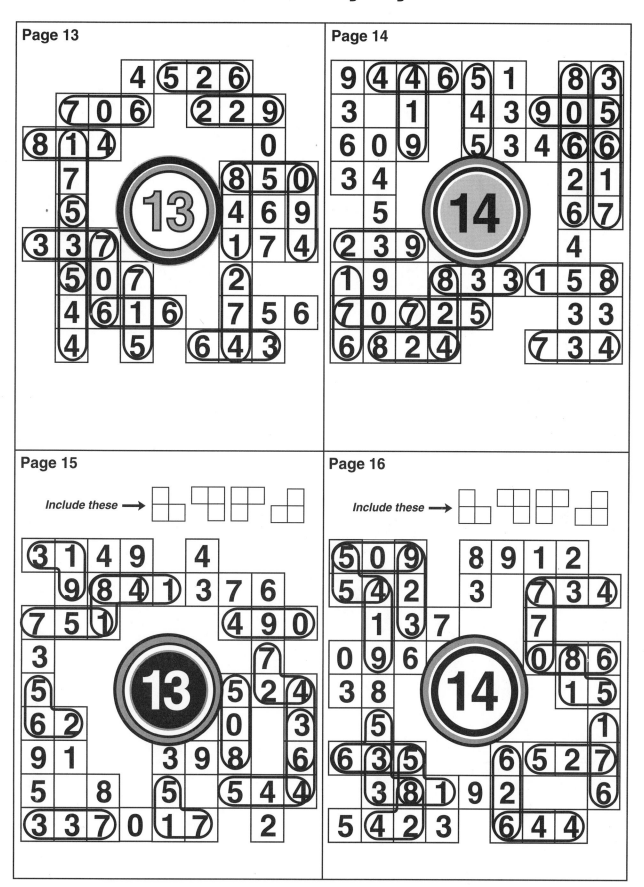

Answers May Vary

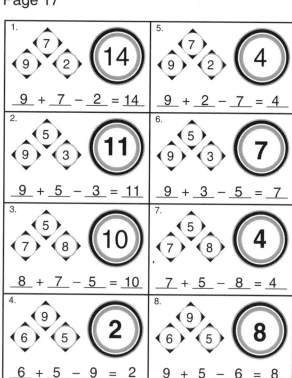

Page 17

1. $9 + 7 - 2 = 14$
2. $9 + 5 - 3 = 11$
3. $8 + 7 - 5 = 10$
4. $6 + 5 - 9 = 2$
5. $9 + 2 - 7 = 4$
6. $9 + 3 - 5 = 7$
7. $7 + 5 - 8 = 4$
8. $9 + 5 - 6 = 8$

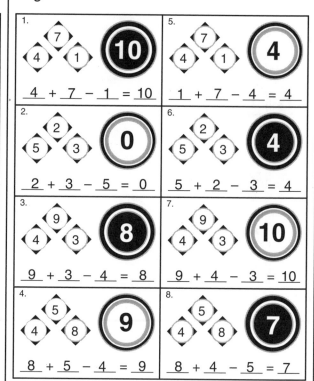

Page 18

1. $4 + 7 - 1 = 10$
2. $2 + 3 - 5 = 0$
3. $9 + 3 - 4 = 8$
4. $8 + 5 - 4 = 9$
5. $1 + 7 - 4 = 4$
6. $5 + 2 - 3 = 4$
7. $9 + 4 - 3 = 10$
8. $8 + 4 - 5 = 7$

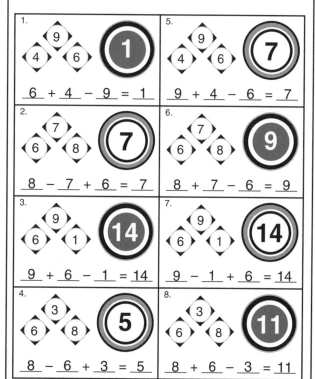

Page 19

1. $6 + 4 - 9 = 1$
2. $8 - 7 + 6 = 7$
3. $9 + 6 - 1 = 14$
4. $8 - 6 + 3 = 5$
5. $9 + 4 - 6 = 7$
6. $8 + 7 - 6 = 9$
7. $9 - 1 + 6 = 14$
8. $8 + 6 - 3 = 11$

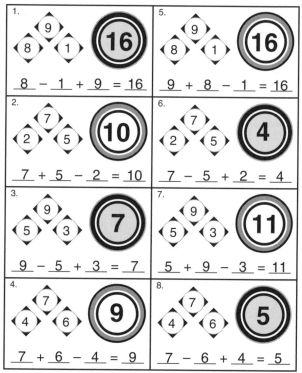

Page 20

1. $8 - 1 + 9 = 16$
2. $7 + 5 - 2 = 10$
3. $9 - 5 + 3 = 7$
4. $7 + 6 - 4 = 9$
5. $9 + 8 - 1 = 16$
6. $7 - 5 + 2 = 4$
7. $5 + 9 - 3 = 11$
8. $7 - 6 + 4 = 5$

Answers May Vary

Page 21

1.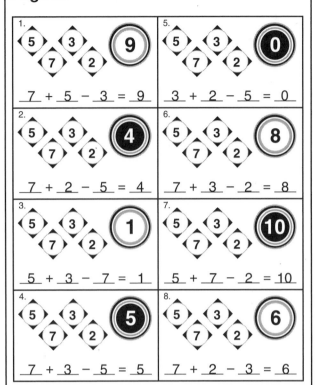
$\underline{9} + \underline{6} - \underline{2} = 13$

5.
$\underline{9} + \underline{2} - \underline{6} = \underline{5}$

2.
$\underline{7} + \underline{6} - \underline{2} = 11$

6.
$\underline{9} + \underline{6} - \underline{7} = \underline{8}$

3.
$\underline{9} + \underline{7} - \underline{6} = 10$

7.
$\underline{7} + \underline{2} - \underline{6} = \underline{3}$

4.
$\underline{2} + \underline{9} - \underline{7} = \underline{4}$

8.
$\underline{9} + \underline{7} - \underline{2} = 14$

Page 22

1.
$\underline{7} + \underline{5} - \underline{3} = \underline{9}$

5.
$\underline{3} + \underline{2} - \underline{5} = \underline{0}$

2.
$\underline{7} + \underline{2} - \underline{5} = \underline{4}$

6.
$\underline{7} + \underline{3} - \underline{2} = \underline{8}$

3.
$\underline{5} + \underline{3} - \underline{7} = \underline{1}$

7.
$\underline{5} + \underline{7} - \underline{2} = 10$

4.
$\underline{7} + \underline{3} - \underline{5} = \underline{5}$

8.
$\underline{7} + \underline{2} - \underline{3} = \underline{6}$

Page 23

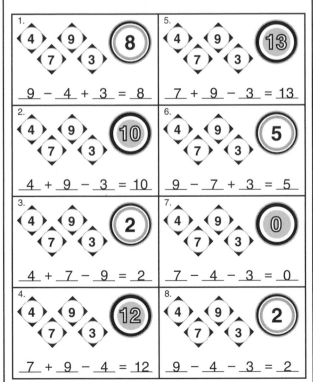

1.
$\underline{9} - \underline{4} + \underline{3} = \underline{8}$

5.
$\underline{7} + \underline{9} - \underline{3} = 13$

2.
$\underline{4} + \underline{9} - \underline{3} = 10$

6.
$\underline{9} - \underline{7} + \underline{3} = \underline{5}$

3.
$\underline{4} + \underline{7} - \underline{9} = \underline{2}$

7.
$\underline{7} - \underline{4} - \underline{3} = \underline{0}$

4.
$\underline{7} + \underline{9} - \underline{4} = 12$

8.
$\underline{9} - \underline{4} - \underline{3} = \underline{2}$

Page 24

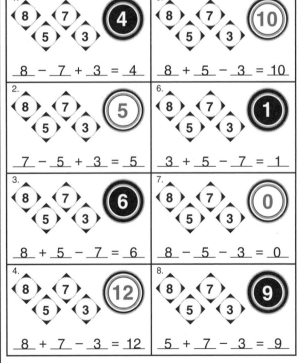

1.
$\underline{8} - \underline{7} + \underline{3} = \underline{4}$

5.
$\underline{8} + \underline{5} - \underline{3} = 10$

2.
$\underline{7} - \underline{5} + \underline{3} = \underline{5}$

6.
$\underline{3} + \underline{5} - \underline{7} = \underline{1}$

3.
$\underline{8} + \underline{5} - \underline{7} = \underline{6}$

7.
$\underline{8} - \underline{5} - \underline{3} = \underline{0}$

4.
$\underline{8} + \underline{7} - \underline{3} = 12$

8.
$\underline{5} + \underline{7} - \underline{3} = \underline{9}$

Answers May Vary

Answers May Vary

Page 29

```
6 9 6 7 0 7 8 3 6 9 1
8 3 1 5 9 8 4 7 8 5 8
6 5 9 4 1 4 3 2 6 3 4
2 7 5 1 7 7 6 4 9 0 6
5 3 6 3 4 4 9 7 6 1 5
```

8

8 4		6 5
4	1.	2. 7

1. $\underline{8} + \underline{4} - \underline{4} = 8$
2. $\underline{6} - \underline{5} + \underline{7} = 8$

9

6	3.	6 4
8 5		4. 7

3. $\underline{6} + \underline{8} - \underline{5} = 9$
4. $\underline{6} - \underline{4} + \underline{7} = 9$

10

5 9	6. 6	
4	5.	1 5

5. $\underline{5} + \underline{9} - \underline{4} = 10$
6. $\underline{6} + \underline{5} - \underline{1} = 10$

11

6	7.	8. 9
8 3		7 5

7. $\underline{6} + \underline{8} - \underline{3} = 11$
8. $\underline{9} - \underline{5} + \underline{7} = 11$

Page 30

```
3 7 2 3 7 8 0 7 5 0 9
0 8 2 6 1 9 7 0 4 8 9
6 0 4 3 8 7 5 0 5 3 4
0 3 9 3 9 3 4 4 1 4 6
1 6 6 8 5 2 2 1 5 3 0
```

7

9 3		9 7
5	1.	2. 5

1. $\underline{9} + \underline{3} - \underline{5} = 7$
2. $\underline{9} - \underline{7} + \underline{5} = 7$

8

3	3.	9 3
6 1		4. 2

3. $\underline{3} + \underline{6} - \underline{1} = 8$
4. $\underline{9} - \underline{3} + \underline{2} = 8$

9

9 7	6. 4	
7	5.	0 5

5. $\underline{9} + \underline{7} - \underline{7} = 9$
6. $\underline{4} + \underline{5} - \underline{0} = 9$

10

4	7.	8. 8
9 3		5 3

7. $\underline{4} + \underline{9} - \underline{3} = 10$
8. $\underline{8} - \underline{3} + \underline{5} = 10$

Page 31

```
4 8 7 4 5 4 7 6 2 6 3
2 8 8 5 6 2 8 3 8 2 2
6 0 6 3 9 5 2 3 7 0 5
7 5 0 9 0 5 8 2 6 1 1
7 0 1 3 5 8 8 1 5 9 9
```

8

3 7		7 0
2	1.	2. 1

1. $\underline{3} + \underline{7} - \underline{2} = 8$
2. $\underline{7} - \underline{0} + \underline{1} = 8$

9

5	3.	9 5
6 2		4. 5

3. $\underline{5} + \underline{6} - \underline{2} = 9$
4. $\underline{9} - \underline{5} + \underline{5} = 9$

10

4 8	6. 5	
2	5.	0 5

5. $\underline{4} + \underline{8} - \underline{2} = 10$
6. $\underline{5} + \underline{5} - \underline{0} = 10$

11

8	7.	8. 8
6 3		5 2

7. $\underline{8} + \underline{6} - \underline{3} = 11$
8. $\underline{8} - \underline{2} + \underline{5} = 11$

Page 32

```
4 0 3 3 8 4 2 4 7 7 5
7 8 8 0 5 3 6 2 7 2 4
7 2 0 5 3 0 2 9 6 8 0
6 7 1 5 8 6 0 9 7 9 4
7 9 8 9 1 9 2 4 0 9 0
```

7

6 8		8 4
7	1.	2. 3

1. $\underline{6} + \underline{8} - \underline{7} = 7$
2. $\underline{8} - \underline{4} + \underline{3} = 7$

8

7	3.	6 0
9 8		4. 2

3. $\underline{7} + \underline{9} - \underline{8} = 8$
4. $\underline{6} - \underline{0} + \underline{2} = 8$

9

4 7	6. 2	
2	5.	2 9

5. $\underline{4} + \underline{7} - \underline{2} = 9$
6. $\underline{2} + \underline{9} - \underline{2} = 9$

10

8	7.	8. 8
2 0		2 0

7. $\underline{8} + \underline{2} - \underline{0} = 10$
8. $\underline{8} - \underline{0} + \underline{2} = 10$

Answers May Vary

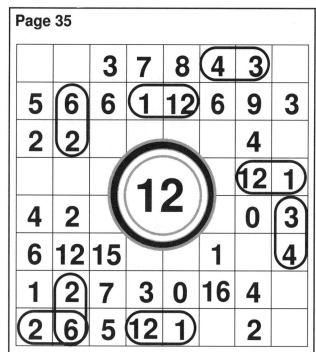

Page 35

		3	7	8	(4	3)	
5	(6	6	(1	12)	6	9	3
2	2)					4	
			12			(12	1)
4	2					0	(3
6	12	15			1		4)
1	(2	7	3	0	16	4	
(2	6)	5	(12	1)		2	

Page 36

4		8	4	(8	4	10	3
7	9	4	5	2)	12	(2	8)
	(4				(16	1)	24
(4	4)		**16**			0	8
	8	0				10	8
3	5	(16			(8	2)	9
6	3	(1	15	7	9	(4	4)
6		9		3	5		2

Page 37

8	(4	5		(3	0	8	
	6)	6	7	4	8)	24	7
3	(12	2)			(12	3	
4	1		**24**		2)	9	
0	17					8	6
(24		(3		5	7	2	
1)	5	(8)	18	4	19	(6	4)
	12	3)	2	10	20		

Page 38

2	10	5	(3	1	3	2	7
7	18	0	(6)	9	3	(6	8
12	(9	2)				3)	9
7	4		**18**			(9	2)
(3	6)					15	3
21	1	(9					3
6	2	2)	4	16	2	(1	18)
10	3	15	4	2	3	9	0

Answers May Vary

Page 39

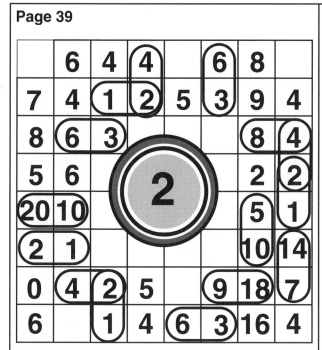

	6	4	4		6	8	
7	4	1	2	5	3	9	4
8	6	3			8	4	
5	6		2		2	2	
20	10				5	1	
2	1				10	14	
0	4	2	5		9	18	7
6		1	4	6	3	16	4

Page 40

18	6	4	9	15	12		
9	3	1	3	5	21	7	36
	33	11				12	4
	5		3			6	18
9	3					2	
0	2					8	
4	12	3	18		18	10	30
36	6	1	24	8	9	27	

Page 41

3	15	5	1	0	2	1	4
10	5	0	4	6	12	3	12
4	20				8	6	
36	4	4			12	2	
9	28				3	12	
24	7				2	8	
8	1	4	6	24	8	3	4
4	0	16	12	6	16	0	1

Page 42

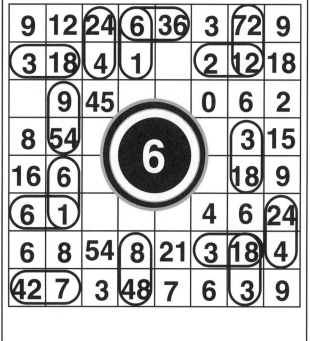

9	12	24	6	36	3	72	9
3	18	4	1		2	12	18
	9	45			0	6	2
8	54	6			3	15	
16	6				18	9	
6	1				4	6	24
6	8	54	8	21	3	18	4
42	7	3	48	7	6	3	9

Answers May Vary

Page 43

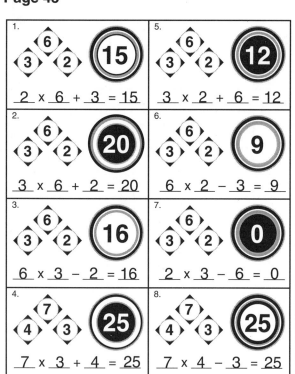

1. $2 \times 6 + 3 = 15$
2. $3 \times 6 + 2 = 20$
3. $6 \times 3 - 2 = 16$
4. $7 \times 3 + 4 = 25$
5. $3 \times 2 + 6 = 12$
6. $6 \times 2 - 3 = 9$
7. $2 \times 3 - 6 = 0$
8. $7 \times 4 - 3 = 25$

Page 44

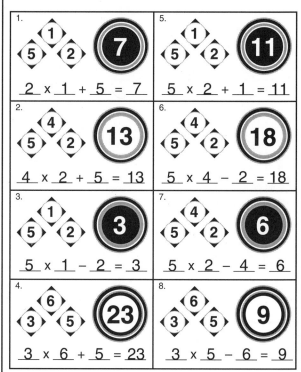

1. $2 \times 1 + 5 = 7$
2. $4 \times 2 + 5 = 13$
3. $5 \times 1 - 2 = 3$
4. $3 \times 6 + 5 = 23$
5. $5 \times 2 + 1 = 11$
6. $5 \times 4 - 2 = 18$
7. $5 \times 2 - 4 = 6$
8. $3 \times 5 - 6 = 9$

Page 45

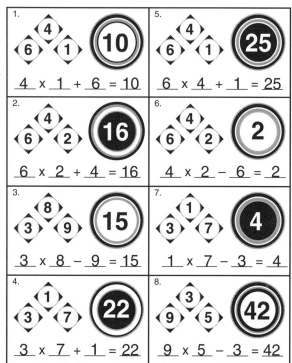

1. $4 \times 1 + 6 = 10$
2. $6 \times 2 + 4 = 16$
3. $3 \times 8 - 9 = 15$
4. $3 \times 7 + 1 = 22$
5. $6 \times 4 + 1 = 25$
6. $4 \times 2 - 6 = 2$
7. $1 \times 7 - 3 = 4$
8. $9 \times 5 - 3 = 42$

Page 46

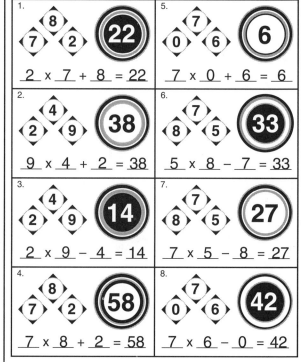

1. $2 \times 7 + 8 = 22$
2. $9 \times 4 + 2 = 38$
3. $2 \times 9 - 4 = 14$
4. $7 \times 8 + 2 = 58$
5. $7 \times 0 + 6 = 6$
6. $5 \times 8 - 7 = 33$
7. $7 \times 5 - 8 = 27$
8. $7 \times 6 - 0 = 42$

Answers May Vary

Page 47

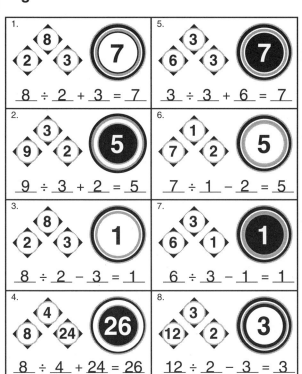

1. $8 \div 2 + 3 = 7$
2. $9 \div 3 + 2 = 5$
3. $8 \div 2 - 3 = 1$
4. $8 \div 4 + 24 = 26$
5. $3 \div 3 + 6 = 7$
6. $7 \div 1 - 2 = 5$
7. $6 \div 3 - 1 = 1$
8. $12 \div 2 - 3 = 3$

Page 48

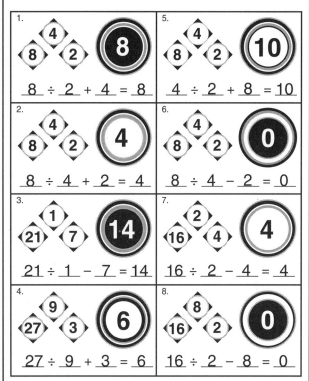

1. $8 \div 2 + 4 = 8$
2. $8 \div 4 + 2 = 4$
3. $21 \div 1 - 7 = 14$
4. $27 \div 9 + 3 = 6$
5. $4 \div 2 + 8 = 10$
6. $8 \div 4 - 2 = 0$
7. $16 \div 2 - 4 = 4$
8. $16 \div 2 - 8 = 0$

Page 49

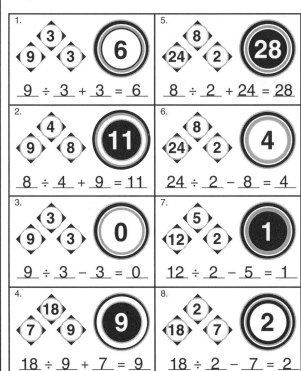

1. $9 \div 3 + 3 = 6$
2. $8 \div 4 + 9 = 11$
3. $9 \div 3 - 3 = 0$
4. $18 \div 9 + 7 = 9$
5. $8 \div 2 + 24 = 28$
6. $24 \div 2 - 8 = 4$
7. $12 \div 2 - 5 = 1$
8. $18 \div 2 - 7 = 2$

Page 50

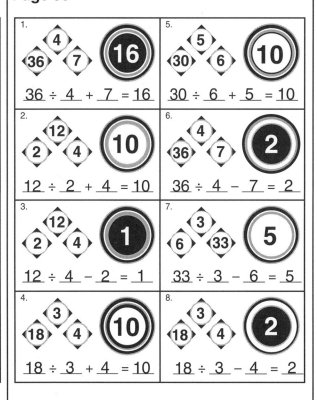

1. $36 \div 4 + 7 = 16$
2. $12 \div 2 + 4 = 10$
3. $12 \div 4 - 2 = 1$
4. $18 \div 3 + 4 = 10$
5. $30 \div 6 + 5 = 10$
6. $36 \div 4 - 7 = 2$
7. $33 \div 3 - 6 = 5$
8. $18 \div 3 - 4 = 2$

Answers May Vary

Page 51

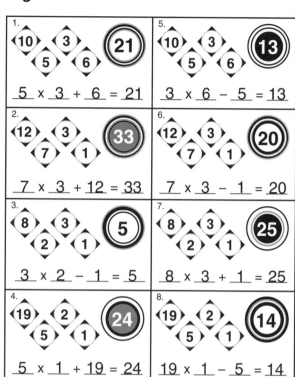

1. 5 x 3 + 6 = 21
2. 7 x 3 + 12 = 33
3. 3 x 2 − 1 = 5
4. 5 x 1 + 19 = 24
5. 3 x 6 − 5 = 13
6. 7 x 3 − 1 = 20
7. 8 x 3 + 1 = 25
8. 19 x 1 − 5 = 14

Page 52

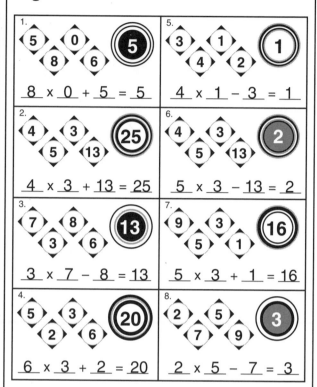

1. 8 x 0 + 5 = 5
2. 4 x 3 + 13 = 25
3. 3 x 7 − 8 = 13
4. 6 x 3 + 2 = 20
5. 4 x 1 − 3 = 1
6. 5 x 3 − 13 = 2
7. 5 x 3 + 1 = 16
8. 2 x 5 − 7 = 3

Page 53

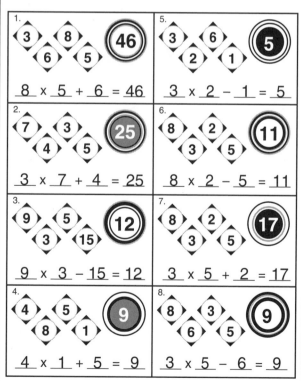

1. 8 x 5 + 6 = 46
2. 3 x 7 + 4 = 25
3. 9 x 3 − 15 = 12
4. 4 x 1 + 5 = 9
5. 3 x 2 − 1 = 5
6. 8 x 2 − 5 = 11
7. 3 x 5 + 2 = 17
8. 3 x 5 − 6 = 9

Page 54

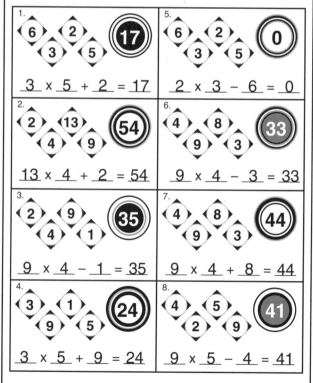

1. 3 x 5 + 2 = 17
2. 13 x 4 + 2 = 54
3. 9 x 4 − 1 = 35
4. 3 x 5 + 9 = 24
5. 2 x 3 − 6 = 0
6. 9 x 4 − 3 = 33
7. 9 x 4 + 8 = 44
8. 9 x 5 − 4 = 41

Answers May Vary

Page 55

1. $12 \div 2 + 9 = 15$
2. $6 \div 2 + 10 = 13$
3. $24 \div 6 - 2 = 2$
4. $6 \div 2 + 7 = 10$
5. $9 \div 3 - 2 = 1$
6. $10 \div 2 - 3 = 2$
7. $27 \div 3 + 1 = 10$
8. $15 \div 3 - 1 = 4$

Page 56

1. $6 \div 2 + 18 = 21$
2. $18 \div 1 + 2 = 20$
3. $18 \div 1 - 2 = 16$
4. $21 \div 3 + 8 = 15$
5. $18 \div 6 - 1 = 2$
6. $18 \div 2 - 6 = 3$
7. $6 \div 3 + 9 = 11$
8. $16 \div 4 - 3 = 1$

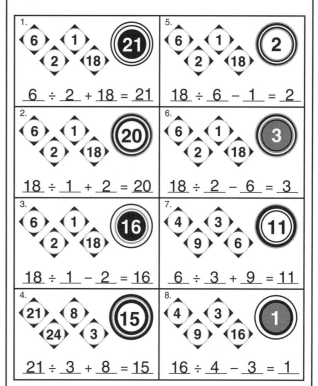

Page 57

1. $10 \div 2 + 3 = 8$
2. $15 \div 3 + 7 = 12$
3. $16 \div 2 - 3 = 5$
4. $22 \div 2 + 10 = 21$
5. $8 \div 2 - 3 = 1$
6. $15 \div 1 - 7 = 8$
7. $4 \div 2 + 16 = 18$
8. $22 \div 1 - 2 = 20$

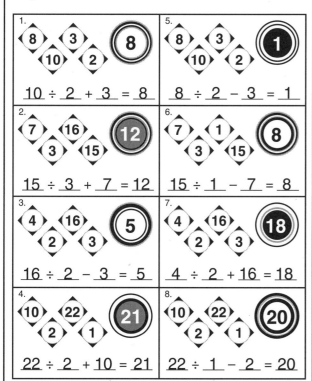

Page 58

1. $24 \div 3 + 2 = 10$
2. $10 \div 2 + 25 = 30$
3. $20 \div 2 - 3 = 7$
4. $14 \div 2 + 9 = 16$
5. $24 \div 3 - 7 = 1$
6. $25 \div 5 - 2 = 3$
7. $21 \div 3 + 2 = 9$
8. $14 \div 2 - 5 = 2$

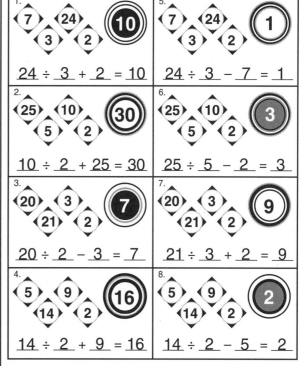

Answers May Vary

Page 61

Parentheses say

"Do Me First"

$(4 \times 5) - 1 = 19$

$4 \times (5 - 1) = 16$

Place parentheses to make these sentences true:

$(3 + 3) \times 2 = 12$ $3 + (3 \times 2) = 9$

$8 \div (2 - 1) = 8$ $(8 \div 2) - 1 = 3$

$(15 - 7) - 2 = 6$ $15 - (7 - 2) = 12$

Page 62

1.
$(8 - 6) \times 7 = 14$

5.
$9 \times (6 + 4) = 90$

2.
$5 + (2 \times 6) = 17$

6.
$4 \times (9 - 6) = 12$

3.
$(5 + 6) \times 2 = 22$

7.
$(9 - 8) \times 3 = 3$

4.
$9 - (6 \div 2) = 6$

8.
$8 \times (3 + 1) = 32$

Page 63

1.
$(5 + 4) \div 3 = 3$

5.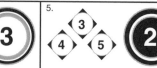
$4 \div (5 - 3) = 2$

2.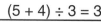
$(5 + 3) \div 4 = 2$

6.
$5 - (8 \div 2) = 1$

3.
$9 - (6 - 2) = 5$

7.
$5 + (8 \times 2) = 21$

4.
$(9 - 6) + 2 = 5$

8.
$(6 + 8) \div 2 = 7$

Page 64

1.
$(6 - 3) \times 8 = 24$

5.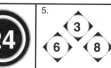
$6 \times (8 - 3) = 30$

2.
$8 \times (6 + 3) = 72$

6.
$(8 - 6) \times 3 = 6$

3.
$(4 - 2) \times 5 = 10$

7.
$5 - (4 - 2) = 3$

4.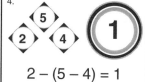
$2 - (5 - 4) = 1$

8.
$2 + (5 \times 4) = 22$

Answers May Vary

Page 65

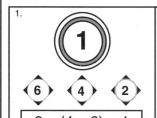

1. $6 \div (4 + 2) = 1$

2. $(8 + 8) \div 8 = 2$

3. $8 - (2 \times 1) = 6$

Any number times 1 equals the original number, and any number divided by itself equals 1.

4. $(8 - 2) + 0 = 6$

Any number plus 0 equals the original number.

Page 66

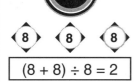
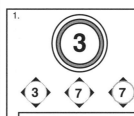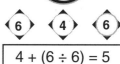
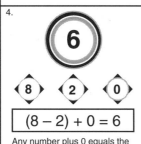

1. $3 + (7 - 7) = 3$

It works because any number plus 0 equals the original number.

2. $4 + (6 \div 6) = 5$

3. $6 + (9 - 8) = 7$

4. $9 - (6 - 5) = 8$

Page 67

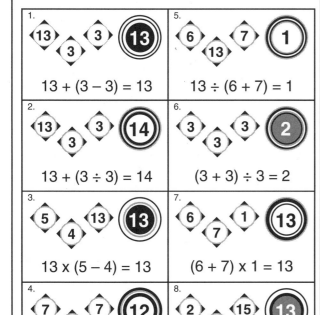

1. $13 + (3 - 3) = 13$

5. $13 \div (6 + 7) = 1$

2. $13 + (3 \div 3) = 14$

6. $(3 + 3) \div 3 = 2$

3. $13 \times (5 - 4) = 13$

7. $(6 + 7) \times 1 = 13$

4. $13 - (7 \div 7) = 12$

8. $15 - 2 - 0 = 13$

Page 68

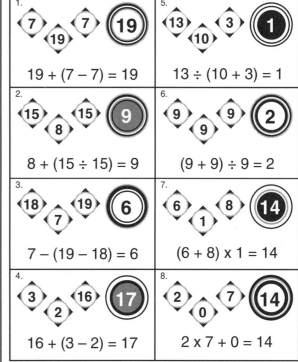

1. $19 + (7 - 7) = 19$

5. $13 \div (10 + 3) = 1$

2. $8 + (15 \div 15) = 9$

6. $(9 + 9) \div 9 = 2$

3. $7 - (19 - 18) = 6$

7. $(6 + 8) \times 1 = 14$

4. $16 + (3 - 2) = 17$

8. $2 \times 7 + 0 = 14$

Answers May Vary

Page 69

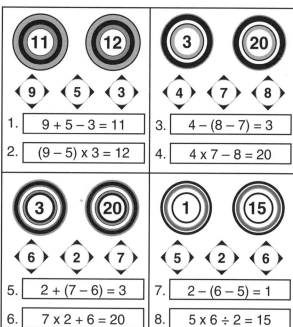

1. $9 + 5 - 3 = 11$
2. $(9 - 5) \times 3 = 12$
3. $4 - (8 - 7) = 3$
4. $4 \times 7 - 8 = 20$

5. $2 + (7 - 6) = 3$
6. $7 \times 2 + 6 = 20$
7. $2 - (6 - 5) = 1$
8. $5 \times 6 \div 2 = 15$

Page 70

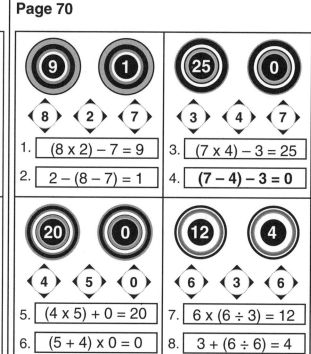

1. $(8 \times 2) - 7 = 9$
2. $2 - (8 - 7) = 1$
3. $(7 \times 4) - 3 = 25$
4. $(7 - 4) - 3 = 0$

5. $(4 \times 5) + 0 = 20$
6. $(5 + 4) \times 0 = 0$
7. $6 \times (6 \div 3) = 12$
8. $3 + (6 \div 6) = 4$

Page 71

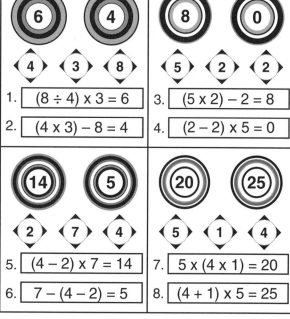

1. $(8 \div 4) \times 3 = 6$
2. $(4 \times 3) - 8 = 4$
3. $(5 \times 2) - 2 = 8$
4. $(2 - 2) \times 5 = 0$

5. $(4 - 2) \times 7 = 14$
6. $7 - (4 - 2) = 5$
7. $5 \times (4 \times 1) = 20$
8. $(4 + 1) \times 5 = 25$

Page 72

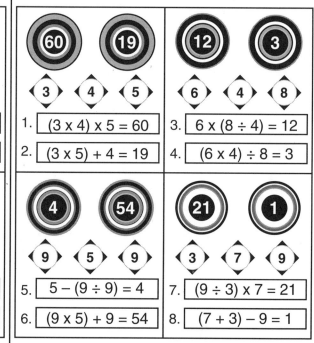

1. $(3 \times 4) \times 5 = 60$
2. $(3 \times 5) + 4 = 19$
3. $6 \times (8 \div 4) = 12$
4. $(6 \times 4) \div 8 = 3$

5. $5 - (9 \div 9) = 4$
6. $(9 \times 5) + 9 = 54$
7. $(9 \div 3) \times 7 = 21$
8. $(7 + 3) - 9 = 1$

Answers May Vary

Page 73

7	2	3	4	2	0	3	7	9	1	6
7	3	1	8	3	8	0	8	6	1	4
3	6	1	6	9	4	7	9	2	7	5
6	4	0	6	8	4	1	6	8	3	3
5	3	6	8	3	9	1	2	1	7	6

(1)
1. $(8 \div 4) - 1 = 1$
2. $(9 - 6) - 2 = 1$

(2)
3. $(4 - 2) - 0 = 2$
4. $(6 \div 1) - 4 = 2$

(3)
5. $(3 \times 8) \div 8 = 3$
6. $(7 - 6) \times 3 = 3$

(4)
7. $6 - (8 - 6) = 4$
8. $(6 - 3) + 1 = 4$

Page 74

4	4	8	0	1	6	3	2	3	1	2
1	9	3	5	8	8	2	0	7	7	1
0	7	2	3	3	9	7	1	3	0	2
6	3	1	4	2	6	0	8	2	1	9
4	7	9	7	5	4	0	6	8	8	3

(5)
1. $6 - (9 - 8) = 5$
2. $(8 - 6) + 3 = 5$

(6)
3. $7 - (3 - 2) = 6$
4. $(3 \times 2) + 0 = 6$

(7)
5. $(8 - 1) + 0 = 7$
6. $(6 + 3) - 2 = 7$

(8)
7. $(6 \times 2) - 4 = 8$
8. $(9 \div 3) + 5 = 8$

Page 75

8	2	9	3	3	5	3	6	3	8	9
7	7	5	1	2	1	8	7	3	1	2
6	9	3	3	2	8	3	2	9	8	2
1	9	5	9	5	3	1	4	4	4	1
6	4	5	3	0	6	5	6	7	8	4

(9)
1. $9 \times (3 \div 3) = 9$
2. $(2 \times 8) - 7 = 9$

(10)
3. $(7 + 3) \times 1 = 10$
4. $(7 \times 2) - 4 = 10$

(11)
5. $2 + 1 + 8 = 11$
6. $9 + 5 - 3 = 11$

(12)
7. $(3 + 3) \times 2 = 12$
8. $(9 - 5) \times 3 = 12$

Page 76

4	1	6	4	5	8	3	0	6	5	6
7	8	9	9	4	6	2	5	9	1	4
1	2	9	5	2	1	8	5	4	1	9
2	5	0	3	5	1	6	4	8	8	7
3	2	0	2	7	3	1	9	5	8	0

(13)
1. $8 + 6 - 1 = 13$
2. $(3 \times 5) - 2 = 13$

(14)
3. $(7 \times 2) + 0 = 14$
4. $(8 + 6) \div 1 = 14$

(15)
5. $8 + 2 + 5 = 15$
6. $(5 \times 2) + 5 = 15$

(16)
7. $9 + 7 + 0 = 16$
8. $(8 \div 4) \times 8 = 16$

Answers May Vary

Page 77

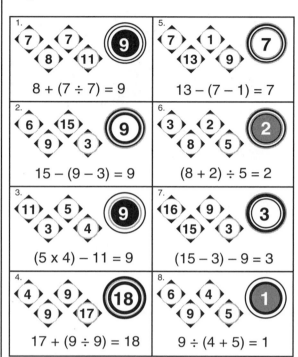

1. $8 + (7 \div 7) = 9$
2. $15 - (9 - 3) = 9$
3. $(5 \times 4) - 11 = 9$
4. $17 + (9 \div 9) = 18$
5. $13 - (7 - 1) = 7$
6. $(8 + 2) \div 5 = 2$
7. $(15 - 3) - 9 = 3$
8. $9 \div (4 + 5) = 1$

Page 78

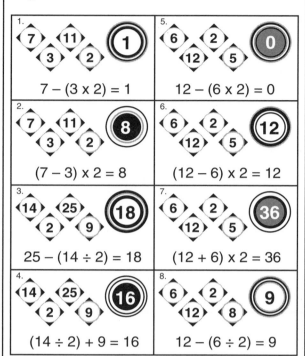

1. $7 - (3 \times 2) = 1$
2. $(7 - 3) \times 2 = 8$
3. $25 - (14 \div 2) = 18$
4. $(14 \div 2) + 9 = 16$
5. $12 - (6 \times 2) = 0$
6. $(12 - 6) \times 2 = 12$
7. $(12 + 6) \times 2 = 36$
8. $12 - (6 \div 2) = 9$

Page 79

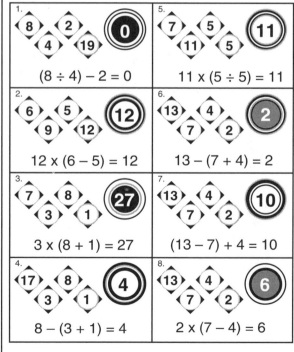

1. $(8 \div 4) - 2 = 0$
2. $12 \times (6 - 5) = 12$
3. $3 \times (8 + 1) = 27$
4. $8 - (3 + 1) = 4$
5. $11 \times (5 \div 5) = 11$
6. $13 - (7 + 4) = 2$
7. $(13 - 7) + 4 = 10$
8. $2 \times (7 - 4) = 6$

Page 80

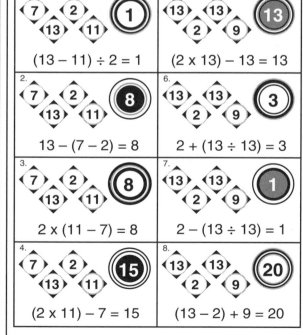

1. $(13 - 11) \div 2 = 1$
2. $13 - (7 - 2) = 8$
3. $2 \times (11 - 7) = 8$
4. $(2 \times 11) - 7 = 15$
5. $(2 \times 13) - 13 = 13$
6. $2 + (13 \div 13) = 3$
7. $2 - (13 \div 13) = 1$
8. $(13 - 2) + 9 = 20$

Answers May Vary

Page 81

Grid:
```
9 6 1 8 2 8 9 4 2 1 2
4 4 5 3 3 7 8 5 2 9 2
8 2 4 0 6 3 9 2 0 2 1
2 5 0 1 6 2 7 8 2 3 3
7 4 3 5 1 5 0 9 6 4 1
```

(10) 37/6 (1.) 23/4 (2.)
1. 6 + 7 − 3 = 10
2. 2 x 3 + 4 = 10

(9) 6/62 (3.) 89/8 (4.)
3. 6 ÷ 2 + 6 = 9
4. 9 − 8 + 8 = 9

(11) 62/1 (5.) 2/78 (6.)
5. 6 x 2 − 1 = 11
6. 8 ÷ 2 + 7 = 11

(9) 8/78 (7.) 2/92 (8.)
7. 8 + 8 − 7 = 9
8. 9 x 2 ÷ 2 = 9

Page 82

Grid:
```
8 2 1 9 1 2 0 4 7 3 8
2 1 3 3 7 4 8 6 3 6 4
4 3 7 6 2 2 2 6 5 1 7
1 8 2 7 6 5 1 5 1 9 2
0 5 4 0 5 9 0 9 5 2 3
```

(5) 51/9 (1.) 21/3 (2.)
1. 9 + 1 − 5 = 5
2. 3 x 1 + 2 = 5

(10) 8/26 (3.) 48/2 (4.)
3. 8 ÷ 2 + 6 = 10
4. 8 − 2 + 4 = 10

(10) 74/2 (5.) 1/19 (6.)
5. 7 x 2 − 4 = 10
6. 9 ÷ 1 + 1 = 10

(10) 6/59 (7.) 3/65 (8.)
7. 6 + 9 − 5 = 10
8. 6 x 5 ÷ 3 = 10

Page 83

Grid:
```
3 2 0 8 6 1 9 7 9 1 2
9 8 1 2 4 2 0 7 8 3 5
1 2 6 7 4 2 5 5 2 7 8
9 6 3 3 9 0 8 1 8 0 2
4 5 6 1 4 5 7 3 2 6 9
```

(10) 78/5 (1.) 42/2 (2.)
1. 8 + 7 − 5 = 10
2. 4 x 2 + 2 = 10

(11) 9/83 (3.) 52/8 (4.)
3. 9 ÷ 3 + 8 = 11
4. 5 − 2 + 8 = 11

(13) 83/2 (5.) 5/81 (6.)
5. 8 x 2 − 3 = 13
6. 8 ÷ 1 + 5 = 13

(12) 8/73 (7.) 6/24 (8.)
7. 8 + 7 − 3 = 12
8. 6 x 4 ÷ 2 = 12

Page 84

Grid:
```
6 1 4 3 8 4 5 3 3 9 8
2 3 5 9 5 8 9 2 3 2 0
1 3 7 3 1 0 1 2 7 6 3
0 8 5 7 2 7 5 5 9 6 4
5 3 6 8 5 7 6 3 1 1 4
```

(7) 95/3 (1.) 10/7 (2.)
1. 9 + 3 − 5 = 7
2. 1 x 0 + 7 = 7

(6) 2/63 (3.) 23/7 (4.)
3. 6 ÷ 2 + 3 = 6
4. 7 − 3 + 2 = 6

(7) 92/1 (5.) 5/36 (6.)
5. 9 x 1 − 2 = 7
6. 6 ÷ 3 + 5 = 7

(8) 7/76 (7.) 3/64 (8.)
7. 7 + 7 − 6 = 8
8. 3 x 8 ÷ 3 = 8

Answers May Vary

Page 89

1.	$8 + 2 \times 4 = 16$	11.	$12 + 6 \times 2 = 24$
2.	$8 \times 2 + 4 = 20$	12.	$12 \times 6 + 2 = 74$
3.	$8 \div 2 + 4 = 8$	13.	$12 \div 6 + 2 = 4$
4.	$8 + 2 \div 4 = 8\frac{1}{2}$	14.	$12 + 6 \div 2 = 15$
5.	$8 \div 2 \times 4 = 16$	15.	$12 \div 6 \times 2 = 4$
6.	$8 \times 2 \div 4 = 4$	16.	$12 \times 6 \div 2 = 36$
7.	$8 - 2 + 4 = 10$	17.	$12 - 6 + 2 = 8$
8.	$8 + 2 - 4 = 6$	18.	$12 + 6 - 2 = 16$
9.	$8 - 2 \times 4 = 0$	19.	$12 - 6 \times 2 = 0$
10.	$8 \times 2 - 4 = 12$	20.	$12 \times 6 - 2 = 70$

Page 90

1.	$(8 + 2) \times (4 - 2) = 14$	13.	$[8 \times (2 + 4)] \div 2 = 18$
2.	$(8 + 2) - (4 \times 2) = 2$	14.	$8 \times [2 \div (4 + 2)] = 6$
3.	$(8 \div 2) + (4 \times 2) = 12$	15.	$[8 + (2 \div 4)] \times 2 = 9$
4.	$(8 \div 2) \times (4 + 2) = 18$	16.	$(8 + 2) \times (4 \div 2) = 12$
5.	$(8 - 2) \times (4 + 2) = 2$	17.	$8 - (2 \div 4) \times 2 = 7$
6.	$[(8 - 2) + 4] \times 2 = 14$	18.	$8 - (2 \times 4) \div 2 = 4$
7.	$8 \times [(2 - 4) \div 2] = 14$	19.	$8 \div [2 - (4 \times 2)] = -4$
8.	$[8 \times (2 \div 4)] - 2 = 2$	20.	$[(8 \div 2) \times 4] - 2 = 14$
9.	$[(8 \div 2) + 4] - 2 = 6$	21.	$(8 + 2) \div (4 - 2) = 6\frac{1}{2}$
10.	$[(8 \div 2) - 4] + 2 = 2$	22.	$8 + [(2 - 4) \div 2] = 8$
11.	$[8 - (2 + 4)] \div 2 = 8$	23.	$8 \times (2 + 4) - 2 = 18$
12.	$8 - [2 \div (4 + 2)] = 9\frac{1}{2}$	24.	$8 \times [2 - (4 + 2)] = 14$

Page 91

1.	$12 + (4 \times 2) = 20$	11.	$12 - (4 \div 2) = 10$
2.	$(12 + 4) \times 2 = 32$	12.	$(12 - 4) \div 2 = 4$
3.	$12 \div (4 + 2) = 2$	13.	$12 \times (4 + 2) = 72$
4.	$(12 \div 4) + 2 = 5$	14.	$(12 \times 4) + 2 = 50$
5.	$12 - (4 \times 2) = 4$	15.	$12 \div (4 \times 2) = 1\frac{1}{2}$
6.	$(12 - 4) \times 2 = 16$	16.	$(12 \div 4) \times 2 = 6$
7.	$12 \times (4 - 2) = 24$	17.	$12 \times (4 \div 2) = 24$
8.	$(12 \times 4) - 2 = 46$	18.	$(12 \times 4) \div 2 = 24$
9.	$12 + (4 - 2) = 14$	19.	$12 \times (4 \times 2) = 96$
10.	$(12 + 4) - 2 = 14$	20.	$(12 \times 4) \times 2 = 96$

Page 92

1.	$(8 + 2) \times (4 - 2) = 20$	13.	$[8 \times (2 + 4)] \div 2 = 24$
2.	$(8 + 2) - (4 \times 2) = 2$	14.	$8 \times [2 \div (4 + 2)] = \frac{8}{3}$
3.	$(8 \div 2) + (4 \times 2) = 12$	15.	$[8 + (2 \div 4)] \times 2 = 17$
4.	$(8 \div 2) \times (4 + 2) = 24$	16.	$(8 + 2) \times (4 \div 2) = 20$
5.	$(8 - 2) \times (4 + 2) = 36$	17.	$8 - (2 \div 4) \times 2 = 7$
6.	$[(8 - 2) + 4] \times 2 = 20$	18.	$8 - (2 \times 4) \div 2 = 4$
7.	$8 \times [(2 - 4) \div 2] = -8$	19.	$8 \div [2 - (4 \times 2)] = -\frac{4}{3}$
8.	$[8 \times (2 \div 4)] - 2 = 2$	20.	$[(8 \div 2) \times 4] - 2 = 14$
9.	$[(8 \div 2) + 4] - 2 = 6$	21.	$(8 + 2) \div (4 - 2) = 5$
10.	$[(8 \div 2) - 4] + 2 = 2$	22.	$8 + [(2 - 4) \div 2] = 7$
11.	$[8 - (2 + 4)] \div 2 = 1$	23.	$8 \times (2 + 4) - 2 = 46$
12.	$8 - [2 \div (4 + 2)] = 7\frac{2}{3}$	24.	$8 \times [2 - (4 + 2)] = -32$